EDTA TITRATIONS

EDTA TITRATIONS

AN INTRODUCTION TO THEORY AND PRACTICE

by

H. A. FLASCHKA

*Professor of Chemistry, Georgia Institute of Technology,
Atlanta, Georgia*

Second edition

PERGAMON PRESS

OXFORD · LONDON · EDINBURGH · NEW YORK
PARIS · FRANKFURT
1964

PERGAMON PRESS LTD.
Headington Hill Hall, Oxford
4 & 5 Fitzroy Square, London W.1

PERGAMON PRESS (SCOTLAND) LTD.
2 & 3 Teviot Place, Edinburgh 1

PERGAMON PRESS INC.
122 East 55th Street, New York 22, N.Y.
GAUTHIER-VILLARS ED.
55 Quai des Grands-Augustins, Paris 6

PERGAMON PRESS G.m.b.H.
Kaiserstrasse 75, Frankfurt am Main

First Published 1959
Second Edition Printed 1964

Library of Congress Catalog Card No. 58–59790

CONTENTS

CONTENTS

FOREWORD

by R. Belcher

WITHIN the space of a few years, ethylenediamine tetra-acetic acid (EDTA) has risen from an obscure chemical compound to the most widely used organic reagent. Elsewhere in this volume reference is made to the enormous amount of literature which has developed. The three text-books which are already available are of an advanced nature and have been written mainly for the practising analyst; from the teaching aspect a gap still remained to be filled. The few texts on the teaching of quantitative inorganic analysis which include exercises on the use of EDTA, rarely go beyond the determination of water-hardness. EDTA is worthy of more extensive treatment not only because of its importance as a titrant, but also because exercises involving its use are a valuable introduction to chelate chemistry. The need for a small teaching text was often expressed in discussions held between Professor Flaschka and the present writer, and resulted in Professor Flaschka preparing this book. It should prove indispensable to teaching institutions at all levels and a useful source of information in routine laboratories. Many of the experiments are suitable for lecture demonstrations.

Professor Flaschka is one of the outstanding analytical chemists of the post-war period and his investigations have played a great part in popularizing the use of EDTA. The value of this book must therefore be enhanced by his wide knowledge of the subject and by his great experience as a teacher.

Birmingham, 1958.

PREFACE

*E*thylene*d*iamine *t*etra-*a*cetic acid is a reagent of remarkable possibilities in both theoretical and applied studies. This was recognized only a short time after the first publications of Dr. G. Schwarzenbach by many workers in many countries. More than 1,200 papers have now appeared on the application of EDTA in analytical chemistry, most of which relate to EDTA titrations. It is thus difficult even for the specialist to select the "best" procedure, indicator, buffer, etc., and the novice is overwhelmed by the flood of publications.

An introductory text such as this, must be incomplete and selective in content. The choice of experiments and the emphasis given to the various topics are a matter of personal preference, but the author will appreciate constructive criticism. A few readily available materials, reagents, and indicators have been selected for emphasis, but the omission of other procedures is *not* intended as silent disapproval. The principles and practical details given here are transferable to new procedures and indicators. An attempt has been made to cover all important types of application for EDTA titrations and full procedural details are given so that the novice can obtain correct results without additional instruction.

Neglect of certain basic facts is the most frequent cause of failure of EDTA titrations; hence, these small, but all-important facts are repeatedly emphasized. In the opening chapters, the general theoretical foundations of EDTA titrations are treated briefly. In addition, each procedure is prefaced by a summary of the relevant theory and background.

Much of the book is based on material prepared by the author for special lectures and university courses. The book should prove valuable for such advanced courses; either as a text-book in its own right or as a supplement to other monographs. The division into sections and sub-sections aids in assigning material and experiments to be covered by students. The problems at the end are of value in ensuring that the student understands the foundations of the method.

As this book is an introductory text, no extensive bibliography is provided. Some important publications are quoted and these should serve as a source of further information. The monographs and reviews cited in section I give full details of the now extensive literature.

The practising analyst has also been kept in mind in the organization of this book. The text should provide sufficient basic knowledge to permit him to adapt procedures given herein or in the journal literature to his special problems.

The author acknowledges with thanks the suggestions made by his many friends and colleagues. He is especially grateful to Drs. Ronald Belcher, Birmingham, A. J. Barnard, Jr., Phillipsburg, and C. N. Reilley, Chapel Hill. The first two have given invaluable aid in organizing the manuscript and in improving the author's imperfect English.

Atlanta, Georgia.   H. FLASCHKA.

December, 1958.

PREFACE TO THE SECOND EDITION

THE booklet was warmly received by readers and reviewers; after only three years the first printing was sold out and a new edition became necessary. Many proposals have been made by readers in letters and discussions as to possible improvements; such constructive criticism was invited by the author and is greatly appreciated. Most proposals dealt with an increase in the number of indicators described, and with an increase in the number of titration procedures. It was a hard decision for the author to follow or not to follow these proposals. It was finally decided not to do so, because it would change the character of the book entirely from being an introductory text. The basic intention of the book was and still is to introduce the reader to the theoretical background and to some practical applications of EDTA titrations. The degree of knowledge gained by working through the booklet should suffice so that any expansion to other indicators and procedures is possible without much difficulty. The only exception has been the inclusion of Xylenol Orange. This indicator has become so important and widely used, and, in addition, is the most outstanding representative of a new type of compound, that it has been described in a separate chapter. Further, its use in the consecutive titration of bismuth and lead has been included. Any other changes have been restricted to the elimination of printing errors, improvement of phraseology, updating of atomic weights to the new scale, small rewritings wherever necessitated by recent knowledge, and the addition of some pertinent new literature references. Some colleagues suggested replacement of experiment 15.2 by the description of a different aluminium titration using a metallochrome indicator. It is true that the redox indication in this experiment is outdated, but the experiment has been retained, because it is such an excellent example of the interaction of complex formation, precipitation and redox reaction, that the author considers it should be retained because of its educational value. Similar reasoning holds in many other cases, for the main emphasis is on types of titration and reaction, and not on their usefulness for actual determination in practical analysis. Thus it is hoped that the character of the book has been maintained, and that its value to the group of readers for which it was written has been increased.

The author again has received help and advice from so many colleagues that it is impossible to list all their names. Only Drs. R. Belcher, Birmingham, and A. Ringbom, Abo, may be named for a special acknowledgement of their assistance.

Atlanta, Ga., July, 1963.   H. FLASCHKA

CHAPTER 1

INTRODUCTION

COMPLEX formation has been applied in chemical analysis for over a century. However, in classical titrimetric analysis only a few applications have been made, of which the titration of cyanide ion with silver according to von Liebig is probably the best known. This limited usage may appear strange, but the explanation is obvious if the essential requirements for the effective use of complex formation (i.e. complexation) in titrimetric procedures are examined. These requirements include:

(a) The complex reaction must be stoicheiometric so that a basis of calculation exists.

(b) The rate of reaction must be sufficiently fast.

(c) The stability of the complexes must be sufficiently high, otherwise a sharp endpoint cannot be obtained because of dissociation.

(d) The complex reaction should involve as few steps as possible so that a sharp endpoint is assured.

(e) A simple method for the location of the endpoint must be known.

(f) No precipitation should occur during the titration to avoid such complications as co-precipitation, adsorption and other phenomena often accompanying precipitation.

Only a few classical cases of complexation meet all of these requirements sufficiently. The greatest obstacle has always been the

9

large number of reaction steps involved in the complexation process (see below), and the lack of suitable indicators.

In the mid-1930s the German firm I.G. Farbenindustrie introduced under the trade name Trilon B, a polyaminocarboxylic acid possessing a remarkable ability to form very stable, water-soluble complexes with many metal ions including the alkaline earths. Among its applications were predicted its uses as a water softener (complexation of calcium and magnesium) and as a textile dyeing assistant (complexation of heavy metals). The systematic name of this substance is ethylene*diamine tetra-acetic* acid, which is now commonly abbreviated to "EDTA" in English-language publications.

The structural formulae for the acid and its disodium salt dihydrate are given in figures 1a–1b.

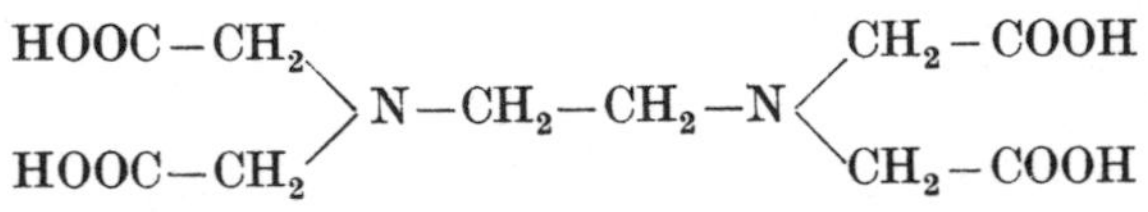

$$\text{HOOC}-\text{CH}_2\diagdown \atop \text{HOOC}-\text{CH}_2\diagup \Big\rangle \text{N}-\text{CH}_2-\text{CH}_2-\text{N} \Big\langle {\diagup \text{CH}_2-\text{COOH} \atop \diagdown \text{CH}_2-\text{COOH}}$$

Figure 1a. Ethylenediamine tetra-acetic acid.

$$\Big[{\text{NaOOC}-\text{CH}_2\diagdown \atop \text{HOOC}-\text{CH}_2\diagup} \Big\rangle \text{N}-\text{CH}_2-\text{CH}_2-\text{N} \Big\langle {\diagup \text{CH}_2-\text{COONa} \atop \diagdown \text{CH}_2-\text{COOH}} \Big] 2\text{H}_2\text{O}$$

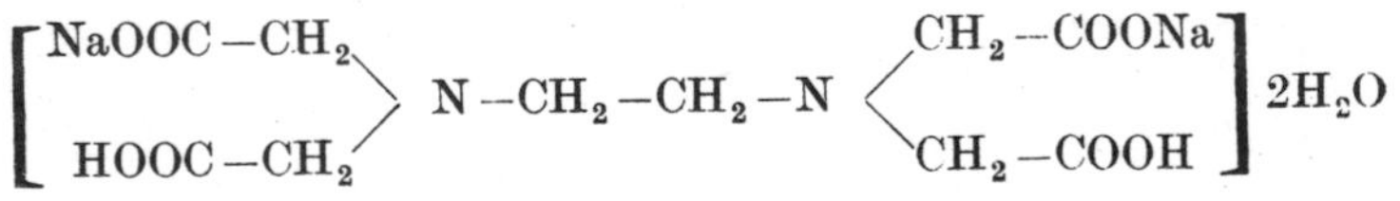

Figure 1b. Disodium ethylenediamine tetra-acetate dihydrate.

At the end of World War II, G. Schwarzenbach, professor at the University of Zürich, Switzerland, and his co-workers initiated physicochemical studies on the metal complexes of EDTA and related compounds, including measurement of their stability constants and reaction mechanisms. In 1946, they introduced EDTA as a titrant and found some metal-sensitive indicators for detecting the endpoint. Thus, a new branch of titrimetric analysis involving chelate formation (see page 13) was originated; this is variously called complexometry, chelatometry or chelometry.

The theoretical studies of Schwarzenbach and co-workers have explained the extraordinary ability of EDTA to form metal complexes, the extreme stability of most of the complexes, and how such complexes can be used in titration processes. Some of the findings of these studies are summarized in the following paragraphs and sections.

The overall stability constant of the copper(II)-tetrammine complex can be expressed as follows and has the indicated value

$$K = \frac{[Cu\ (NH_3)_4^{+2}]}{[Cu^{+2}] \times [NII_3]^4} = 4 \cdot 4 \times 10^{12} \tag{1.1}$$

In contrast, the stability of the magnesium–EDTA complex is given as

$$K = \frac{[MgY^{-2}]}{[Mg^{+2}] \times [Y^{-4}]} = 4 \cdot 9 \times 10^8 \tag{1.2}$$

Y^{-4} denotes the anion of EDTA. Magnesium can be titrated with EDTA accurately; but copper cannot be titrated with aqueous ammonia despite the higher stability of the copper-tetrammine complex. Bjerrum has demonstrated that complexes possessing more than one ligand attached to the central ion are formed stepwise. Hence, the formation of the copper-tetrammine complex may be expressed as follows:

$$Cu^{+2} \underset{-NH_3}{\overset{+NH_3}{\rightleftarrows}} Cu(NH_3)^{+2} \underset{-NH_3}{\overset{+NH_3}{\rightleftarrows}} Cu(NH_3)_2^{+2} \underset{-NH_3}{\overset{+NH_3}{\rightleftarrows}}$$

$$Cu(NH_3)_3^{+2} \underset{-NH_3}{\overset{+NH_3}{\rightleftarrows}} Cu(NH_3)_4^{+2} \tag{1.3}$$

For each step, the law of mass action is applicable and for each of the complexes a stability constant may be written:

$$K_1 = \frac{[Cu(NH_3)^{+2}]}{[Cu^{+2}] \times [NH_3]} = 1\cdot4 \times 10^4 \qquad (1.4a);$$

$$K_2 = \frac{[Cu(NH_3)_2{}^{+2}]}{[Cu(NH_3)^{+2}] \times [NH_3]} = 3\cdot1 \times 10^3 \qquad (1.4b);$$

$$K_3 = \frac{[Cu(NH_3)_3{}^{+2}]}{[Cu(NH_3)_2{}^{+2}] \times [NH_3]} = 7\cdot8 \times 10^2 \qquad (1.4c);$$

$$K_4 = \frac{[Cu(NH_3)_4{}^{+2}]}{[Cu(NH_3)_3{}^{+2}] \times [NH_3]} = 1\cdot3 \times 10^2 \qquad (1.4d)$$

Naturally each of these constants is smaller in value than the overall constant which is the product $K = K_1 \times K_2 \times K_3 \times K_4$.

Therefore the disappearance of the "free" copper ion on addition of ammonia at the point where $Cu:NH_3 = 1:4$ (endpoint of a suggested titration) will be not as abrupt as in the case of magnesium. Here a $1:1$ complex is formed in a single step. (For a more comprehensive and mathematical treatment of complexation see chapter 4, page 24.)

Schwarzenbach has demonstrated that a remarkable increase in stability is achieved if *two* monodentate ligands (these are ligands which can occupy only one co-ordinate position at the central ion) are replaced by *one* bidentate ligand (i.e. a ligand able to occupy two co-ordinate positions). If ammonia is replaced by the bidentate ligand ethylenediamine, $NH_2 \cdot CH_2 \cdot CH_2 \cdot NH_2$, only a two-step reaction is necessary to co-ordinate four nitrogens to the copper. The stability constants of the two complexes $Cu(en)_1^{+2}$ and $Cu(en)_2^{+2}$, where *en* denotes ethylenediamine, are 6×10^{10} and 2×10^9 respectively. A remarkable gain in stability can be noted if these figures are compared with the corresponding data on the formation of the copper-tetrammine complex.

If ammonia is replaced by the tetradentate ligand triethylenetetrammine, $NH_2 \cdot CH_2 \cdot CH_2 \cdot NH \cdot CH_2 \cdot CH_2 \cdot NH \cdot CH_2 \cdot CH \cdot NH_2$, only one single step is necessary to attach four nitrogens to the copper. The stability constant of the 1:1 complex formed is 4×10^{20}. Thus, compared with the tetrammine complex, a relative increase of about 10^8 is effected by substituting the polyamine for ammonia.

Complexes formed with polydentate ligands are called chelate complexes or simply chelates. The term is derived from the Greek "chele" for a claw such as that of the crab, and is appropriate because the ligand "grasps" the central ion from at least two sides. The gain in stability of a complex by replacing n monodentate ligands by a single analogous n-dentate ligand is called the chelate effect. This effect generally reaches its maximum if the rings formed are five or six membered. Rings with fewer members possess considerable strain, and hence are much lower in stability. A greater number of members in the ring also results in lower stability because of an entropic effect. In simple terms, if the chain between the active group in the ligand becomes too long, they behave more and more as isolated monodentate groups. Thus, through chelate formation two important requirements for titration procedures are achieved: an increase in stability of the complex and a decrease in the number of reaction steps in the complexation process.

With the above facts in mind, it is easily appreciated why only a few "classical" complexes are capable of providing the necessary basis for a titration procedure. Noteworthy examples include the titration of cyanide with silver, and of chloride with mercury. Silver forms a very stable cyano complex and shows a coordination number of only two. Mercury has a coordination number of four, but the distribution of the overall stability within the four stepwise complexes is unusual. The log K-value for the four chloro-complexes are approximately 7,7,3, and -1. Thus in the chloride titration mercury behaves as though it exhibits only a coordination number of two.

The structure of EDTA is such that the most favourable combination of carboxylic groups (for salt formation) and amino nitrogen (for co-ordinate bonds) is achieved. All rings in the complex are five membered as shown in the figure on page 14.

Thus, EDTA forms complexes with nearly all polyvalent metal ions and also with many monovalent cations, including alkali metals (with the latter only to a slight extent). Practically all these complexes contain metal and EDTA in the ratio 1 : 1, regardless of the valency of the metal ion.

Though EDTA is frequently used as titrant, this is not its only analytical application. Growing interest exists in EDTA as a masking reagent to prevent interference and to increase the selectivity of tests. EDTA is used as a chromogenic agent in spectrophotometric procedures and plays an important rôle in polarography and ion exchange procedures. Its application in non-analytical fields is wide-spread.

The literature on the analytical applications of EDTA is extensive and has long passed the number of 2000 publications. It is impossible to cite even a selection of only the most important references

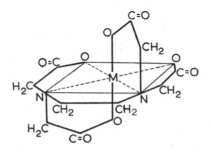

Figure 2. Steric configuration of a metal–EDTA complex. (According to A. E. Martell, *J. Chem. Education,* **29,** 270 (1952).)

in a booklet such as this. Accordingly, the bare minimum number of references is quoted, but there is sufficient indication of sources of further information. For more complete details the reader's attention may be called to the following standard works:

G. Schwarzenbach: *Die komplexometrische Titration.* F. Encke, Stuttgart, 2nd edition (1956). English translation (H. Irving): *Complexometric Titration.* Methuen, London (1957).

F. J. Welcher: *The Analytical Use of EDTA.* Van Nostrand, Princeton (1958).

R. Přibil: *Komplexone in der chemischen Analyse.* VEB Deutscher

Verlag der Wissenschaften, Berlin (1961). This is an updated and revised translation of the 1957 Czech edition.

L. Meites (editor): *Handbook of Analytical Chemistry*. McGraw-Hill, New York (1963). The section on complexometric titrations by Reilley, Barnard and Püschel contains extensive tabulation of titration procedures, stability constants, and indicators, with accompanying references to the original literature.

Many reviews have been published. One of these, covering the literature to 1958 as completely as possible is a series of publications by the following authors:

A. J. Barnard, W. C. Broad and H. Flaschka: The EDTA Titration: Nature and Methods of Endpoint Detection. *Chemist Analyst*, **45**, 86, 111 (1956); **46**, 18, 46, 76 (1957).

H. Flaschka, A. J. Barnard and W. C. Broad: The EDTA Titration: Applications. *Chemist Analyst*, **46**, 22 (1957); **47**, 22, 52, 78, 109 (1958).

The review section in the British journal "Chemistry and Industry" brings in regular intervals articles concerning new developments in analytical chemistry including complexometric titrations.

CHAPTER 2

EDTA. THE ACID, ITS SALTS AND COMPLEXES

ETHYLENEDIAMINE TETRA-ACETIC ACID, as already mentioned, is now commonly abbreviated EDTA. However, it should be noted that the abbreviation can also mean acetate and does so in most cases, because the free acid is seldom used in analytical procedures. Generally, it can easily be seen from the text whether the meaning is acid or acetate; if a special differentiation is to be made "EDTA acid" might be used.

The letter Y is used generally to denote the anion of the EDTA acid in writing formulae either with charges, e.g. Y^{-4}, or without. Charge signs in formulations are frequently omitted because they are usually unimportant.

EDTA is marketed under various trade names including: Chelaton II and III* (Czechoslovakia), Complexone II and III* (Siegfried, Switzerland), Idranal II and III* (Riedel de Haen, Germany), Sequestrene (Geigy, U.S.A.), Sequestrol (Geigy, England), Titriplex (Merck, Germany), and Versene (Dow, U.S.A.). In Russian literature the name Trilon B is frequently encountered. These are the most important ones so far as analytical grade products are concerned. Salts and complexes are also named chelonates, complexonates, versenates or trilonates.

EDTA is a white, crystalline powder, odourless and with an acid taste. It is not poisonous. It is sparingly soluble in water (0·02 g in 100 ml water at 22° C). It is insoluble in acids and common organic solvents, but is soluble in caustic and ammonia solutions. From such solutions, the acid can be precipitated by addition of mineral acids—a common and simple method of purification. It is stable at elevated

* II refers to the free acid, III to the disodium salt dihydrate.

16

temperatures and melts at $241 \cdot 5°$ C; it is non-hygroscopic and crystallizes without water. The molecular weight is $292 \cdot 25$ The structure has already been given in figure 1a (see page 10).

The dissociation constants of the hydrogens of the four carboxylic groups have been measured by Schwarzenbach. The numerical values expressed in pk (i.e. the negative logarithms of the dissociation constant) are $pk_1 = 2 \cdot 0$, $pk_2 = 2 \cdot 67$, $pk_3 = 6 \cdot 16$, $pk_4 = 10 \cdot 3$. Only two of these hydrogens are strongly acidic and this led Schwarzenbach to suggest a zwitterion or betaine structure (see figure 3).

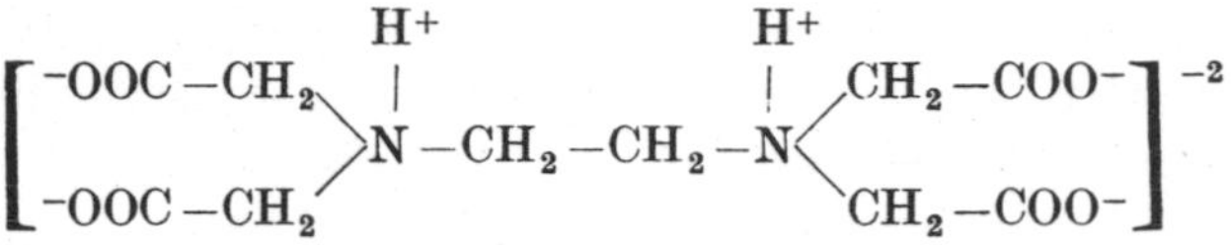

$$\begin{bmatrix} \text{-OOC-CH}_2 \overset{\overset{\displaystyle \text{H}^+}{|}}{\diagdown} & \overset{\overset{\displaystyle \text{H}^+}{|}}{} \\ \diagup \text{N-CH}_2\text{-CH}_2\text{-N} \diagdown & \\ \text{-OOC-CH}_2 & \text{CH}_2\text{-COO}^- \end{bmatrix}^{-2}$$

Figure 3. Double betaine structure of EDTA.

Recent infra-red analysis, however, seems to indicate that the hydrogens form a hydrogen bond between two carboxylic groups. Whatever the structure may be, the fact remains that the two weakly bonded hydrogens are released during complex formation (see experiment 3.9, page 21). Naturally the extent to which the hydrogens are bonded to the molecule depends upon the pH of the solution; the degree of proton-dissociation is less the more acidic the solution. In general, it is usual to take care of this fact by writing EDTA in reaction schemes always as H_2Y^{-2}. The pH effect allied with the complex formation is of the greatest importance for titrations. It is the main reason why the pH of the solution being titrated must be kept constant or at least held within certain limits. (See chapter 13, page 74.)

Of the four possible sodium salts the disodium dihydrate, $Na_2H_2Y \cdot 2H_2O$, is the one used almost exclusively in analytical chemistry. Some properties are described in chapter 11, page 64.

Many metal-EDTA complexes have been prepared and their properties have been studied. For example, if calcium carbonate and EDTA are slurried in equivalent amounts with water, during boiling solubilization occurs, and after evaporation the complex $CaH_2Y \cdot nH_2O$ crystallizes. If two equivalents of calcium carbonate are treated with one equivalent of EDTA acid, a compound $Ca_2Y \cdot nH_2O$ is formed. In this compound half of the calcium is ionically bonded and can be precipitated with oxalate from an ammoniacal solution of the compound. The other half of the calcium is complexed and does not react with oxalate. If calcium carbonate is treated with an equivalent amount of a solution of Na_2H_2Y, on crystallization a compound $Na_2CaY \cdot nH_2O$ is obtained.

All the compounds named above exist with various amounts of water of crystallization depending on the procedure of preparation. Analogous salt-like and complex compounds have been prepared with other metal ions and EDTA. Some of them are used in EDTA titrations and are available commercially. Especially important are $Na_2MgY \cdot 4H_2O$ and the corresponding zinc and copper compounds. The preparation of solutions of the magnesium-EDTA and copper-EDTA complexes is described in chapter 12, page 69.

CHAPTER 3

EXPERIMENTS WITH EDTA COMPLEXES

SOME theoretical considerations and a mathematical treatment of the formation and stability of metal-EDTA complexes are given in chapter 4. At this point some experiments are described and explained to provide practical experience with these reactions. The preparation of the necessary solutions is described in chapter 12, page 69. It is very convenient to place the reagents in dropping-bottles, stored in a rack such as is used for semimicro qualitative analysis courses.

Complex formation can easily be demonstrated when it is accompanied by a colour change.

Experiment 3.1: Place 3 drops of 0·1 M copper(II) ion solution in a test-tube and wash down with 5 ml of water. Add 5 drops of buffer pH 10. The deep colour of the copper tetrammine complex develops. Now add dropwise 0·1 M EDTA and shake after each addition. Note the gradual change to a much lighter blue colour which is the colour of the copper–EDTA complex.

A colour change can also be observed, when nickel or cobalt are complexed. The colours, however, are less intense and therefore more concentrated solutions must be used.

Experiment 3.2: Place 5 drops of 0·1 M nickel solution and 2 drops of buffer pH 5 in a test-tube and add dropwise 0·1 M EDTA solution. Note that the colour turns to green-blue.

Experiment 3.3: Place 5 drops of 0·1 M cobalt solution and 2 drops of buffer pH 10 in a test-tube. Add dropwise 0·1 M EDTA solution. Note that the colour changes from yellow to pink.

The complex formation in the previous experiments took place very rapidly (except possibly in the case of nickel), but some complexes form very slowly, for example, that of chromium.

19

Experiment 3.4: Place 5 drops of 0.1 M chromium(III) solution and 2 drops of buffer pH 5 in a test-tube. Wash down with 5 ml of water and add 5 drops of 0.1 M EDTA solution. No colour change occurs even after standing for 30 min or more. Heat the solution to boiling. Note that soon a brilliant deep violet develops.

The chromium in the original solution was not present as "free" chromium ion, but as sulphato, aquo, chloro, acetato or mixed complex depending on the anions present in the solution. These complexes react very slowly.

Experiment 3.5: Place 5 drops of 0.1 M potassium dichromate solution and 3 drops of buffer pH 5 in a test-tube. Add 6 drops of 0.1 M EDTA solution and wash down with 3 ml of water. Add a few crystals of ascorbic acid. Note the rapid development of the violet colour of the chromium-EDTA complex.

During the reduction of chromate by the ascorbic acid some intermediate species occur which complex rapidly with EDTA and do so before an acetato, sulphato, chloro or other complex is formed. Thus it can be shown that the release of chromium from this type of complex is the rate determining step in the reaction taking place in experiment 3.4.

The complexes formed in the experiments described above are the normal complexes obtained according to the general reaction scheme: $Me^{+n} + Y^{-4} = MeY^{+n-4}$. In addition there exist hydrogen and hydroxo complexes, the formation of which is sometimes also accompanied by a colour change.

Experiment 3.6: Place 5 drops of 0.1 M iron(III) solution into a test-tube and dilute with 5 ml of water. Check the pH and adjust if necessary to about 2–3. Add dropwise 0.1 M EDTA solution. Note the development of a yellow colour which is the colour of the normal complex FeY^{-1}. Now add dropwise 0.1 M sodium hydroxide and shake after each addition. Note the colour change from yellow to brown. Add 2 drops of 2 M sodium hydroxide. The solution becomes turbid owing to the formation of hydrated ferric oxide.

The reaction scheme is as follows:

$$\mathrm{FeY^{-1} \underset{-OH^-}{\overset{+OH^-}{\rightleftarrows} } Fe(OH)Y^{-2} \underset{-OH^-}{\overset{+OH^-}{\rightleftarrows}} Fe(OH)_2 Y^{-3} \underset{-OH^-}{\overset{+OH^-}{\rightleftarrows}} Fe(OH)_3 + Y^{-4}} \quad (3.1)$$

yellow pH $= 6$ brown   pH $= 10.5$

The more alkaline the solution, the more OH^- ions are present in the complex, and the weaker is the binding between iron and EDTA. At pH about 10·5 the complex is disrupted and hydrated ferric oxide is precipitated.

The formation of a hydroxo complex is also accompanied by a colour change in the case of chromium.

Experiment 3.7: Place 3 drops of 0·1 M chromium(III) solution, 1 drop of buffer pH 5 and 3 drops of 0·1 M EDTA solution in a test-tube. Dilute with 5 ml of water and heat to boiling. If the violet normal complex has formed, add dropwise 0·1 M sodium hydroxide solution. Note the sudden colour change from violet to clear blue, which is the colour of the hydroxo complex, $Cr(OH)Y^{-2}$.

Interesting colour reactions take place with some metal-EDTA complexes after adding hydrogen peroxide, owing to oxidation effects and/or formation of peroxo complexes. These colours are extremely deep and the reactions can be used as a basis for the photometric determination of some of the metals.

Experiment 3.8: Place 2 drops of a 0·1 M iron(III) solution, 5 drops of 0·1 M EDTA solution and 3 drops of buffer pH 10 in a test-tube and dilute with water to about 5 ml. Add 2 drops of 3 per cent hydrogen peroxide. Note the very intense violet colour caused by the formation of the complex $Fe(H_2O_2)Y^{-1}$. Note further that the colour fades after some time owing to the reduction of the hydrogen peroxide.

The formation of metal-EDTA complexes can be shown indirectly for systems where no colour reaction is involved. As pointed out in chapter 2, page 16, EDTA exists in a nearly neutral solution largely in the form H_2Y^{-2}. The two weakly bound hydrogens are released during the complex formation and the solution becomes acidic according to the reaction

$$M^{+2} + H_2Y^{-2} \xrightleftharpoons{} MY^{-2} + 2 H^+ \qquad (3.2)$$

This increase in acidity can easily be shown by addition of an appropriate acid-base indicator.

Experiment 3.9: Place 5 drops of 0·1 M cobalt(II), 8 drops of 0·1 M EDTA and 3 drops of 2 N NaOH into a test tube and dilute with 5 ml of water. Note the appearance of a barely visible dull pink colour. Now add 5 drops of 2% hydrogen peroxide and observe a colour change to an intense blue. Add dropwise 1 : 2 nitric acid until the colour changes to a brilliant red. Add again 2 N NaOH and observe the colour changing back to the blue. Bring back to red with a few drops of nitric acid and heat to boiling. Allow to stand until the solution is at room temperature and add dropwise 2 N NaOH. Observe that the colour change to blue does not occur until quite an excess of base has been added, and that even then the change is only slow.

Many interesting reactions are taking place during this experiment. The original faintly dull pink colour of the alkaline solution is due to the complex Co(OH)Y^{-3} containing Co(II). Upon addition of hydrogen peroxide the complex Co(OH)Y^{-2} is formed via the oxidation of Co(II) to Co(III). Note the contrast with the preceding experiment where a peroxo complex was formed! Upon addition of acid the following reaction takes place

$$Co(OH)Y^{2-} + H^+ \rightleftarrows Co(H_2O)Y^-$$

The Co(III) is now coordinated to one EDTA and one water molecule. This reaction is readily reversible upon addition of base. However, after standing for some time the water is expelled from the complex in a slow reaction, and the complex CoY$^-$ (still with Co(III) in it) is formed. Warming the solution hastens this reaction. Now upon addition of base the proton transfer is no longer possible with ease and the colour change to blue does not occur unless much base is added. With a high concentration of base an OH-ion is forced back into the complex and the blue colour is restored. With the newly formed Co(OH)Y^{-2} the rapid indicator-like colour changes, from blue to red and back, can be produced again.

Frequently an organic ligand, which in the free form is readily oxidized, is stabilized against oxidation when combined with a metal ion to form a complex. This is demonstrated in the following experiment.

Experiment 3.10: Place in each of two test tubes 8 drops of 0·1 M EDTA and 10 drops of 0·1 M acetic acid and dilute with about 5 ml of water. One tube is not treated further and is marked I. The other is marked as tube II, and in addition to its contents 5 drops of 0·1 M chromium(III) solution are added. Tube II is heated to boiling and set aside for complete development of the violet chromium-EDTA complex (see experiment 3·4). The solution in tube I is brought to boiling and 0·2 M potassium permanganate solution is added drop by drop. As in the titration of oxalic acid, the decolourization of the first drop is slow, with further drops the colour fades more rapidly. Wait for complete or nearly complete decolourization before the next drop is added. EDTA is oxidized and when no EDTA is left, the permanganate oxidizes the manganese(II) formed to hydrated MnO$_2$ and itself is reduced to this compound. A brownish black slurry forms. Next add one drop of concentrated hydrogen peroxide and observe the solution become rapidly clear and colourless.

Now repeat the same procedure with tube I. It will be noticed that the thick brown slurry will occur after the addition of a smaller number of drops of permanganate, because here only three drops of EDTA (the excess over the 5 drops of chromium solution) need be oxidized, while in the first part of the experiment 8 drops of EDTA have been oxidized. Remove again the slurry of hydrous Mn(IV)-oxide by addition of one drop of hydrogen peroxide and note that the original violet colour of the chromium(III)-EDTA complex is still present.

Experiment 3.11: Place in a test-tube 5 drops of a 0·1 M magnesium solution and dilute to about 3 ml with water. In another test-tube place 5 drops of 0·1 M EDTA solution and dilute to about 3 ml. Place in each test-tube 1 drop 0·1 per cent methyl red solution. To each tube add dropwise 0·1 M hydrochloric acid until the colour turns to red. Then add 0·1 M sodium hydroxide until the colour just turns back to orange or yellow. Now mix the two solutions. Observe that the colour changes to red which indicates a decrease of pH.

This pH effect is an extremely important consideration in any EDTA titration. It is necessary to have adequate buffering or close control of pH to avoid any significant drop in the latter during the titration.

Some more experiments may be found in the reference given below.

Bibliography

(1) EDTA and complex formation. A demonstration lecture.
M. B. Johnston, A. J. Barnard jr. and H. Flaschka., *J. Chem. Educat.* **35**, 601 (1958).

CHAPTER 4

THE STABILITY CONSTANTS OF EDTA COMPLEXES

(1) The absolute stability constant.

If only the fully ionized anion of EDTA is taken into consideration the complex formation between a metal M^{+n}, of the oxidation state n, and Y^{-4} takes place according to the equilibrium

$$M^{+n} + Y^{-4} \rightleftarrows MY^{+n-4} \tag{4.1}$$

Applying the law of mass action the equilibrium constant is given by

$$K = \frac{[MY^{+n-4}]}{[M^{+n}] \times [Y^{-4}]} \tag{4.2}$$

This constant is called the *stability constant* or *formation constant*. The reciprocal, $1/K$, is called the *dissociation constant* or *instability constant*. To differentiate this constant from the *apparent stability constant* defined in (4.3), (4.11) and more generally in (4.18) it is convenient to name it the *absolute stability constant*. This term, however, should not be confused with the notation *thermodynamical constant*. The absolute stability constant is a concentration constant and is expressed as measured at a certain ionic strength, whereas the thermodynamic constant is valid only for ionic strength equal to zero.

(2) The apparent stability constant.

The absolute stability constant is defined in terms of only the EDTA that is present in the completely dissociated form Y^{-4}. The metal ion concentration refers to the "free" metal, that is, not

24

TABLE 1

Stability constants of the normal EDTA complexes of some common metals according to Schwarzenbach (see Bibliography, page 14). The constants are the absolute ones and valid for a medium of ionic strength 0·1 at 20° C.

Cation	log K	Cation	log K
Ag^+	7·3	Cd^{+2}	16·46
Ba^{+2}	7·76	Zn^{+2}	16·50
Sr^{+2}	8·63	Pb^{+2}	18·04
Mg^{+2}	8·69	Ni^{+2}	18·62
Ca^{+2}	10·70	Cu^{+2}	18·80
Mn^{+2}	13·79	Hg^{+2}	21·80
Fe^{+2}	14·33	Cr^{+3}	23·0
Al^{+3}	16·13	Th^{+4}	23·2
Co^{+2}	16·31	Fe^{+3}	25·1

complexed with EDTA, and present solely as the aquo complex. The EDTA, however, will be present totally as Y^{-4} only in strongly alkaline solution at a pH higher than 10. At lower pH values the uncombined EDTA will be present also in its protonated forms HY^{-3}, H_2Y^{-2}, H_3Y^{-1} and H_4Y. These forms will vary in their amounts according to the pH of the solution. To account for this fact, the stability constant under the actual solution conditions must be calculated, and the resulting constant is called the *apparent, conditional or effective stability constant*. A factor a_H (the subscript denotes the H^+ dependence) can be used to calculate the apparent from the absolute stability constant.

In solutions another complex-forming substance may be present in addition to EDTA. Then according to the stability constants of the complexes formed with the metal and this substance, more or less of the metal is transferred to those complexes. $[M^{+n}]$ can no longer be considered to be the *total* amount of "free" metal ion though it is the total amount of metal not complexed with EDTA. To account for that effect a factor β_A may be introduced.

The calculation of these factors, a_H and β_A, is explained in the following paragraphs. In order to evaluate the titration conditions and to understand what is going on in the course of a titration, it is important to become completely familiar with these two factors.

(3) Influence of pH.

At any pH the apparent stability constant may be expressed by:

$$K_{\text{ap.H}} = \frac{[MY^{+n-4}]}{[M^{+n}] \times [Y]^*} \tag{4.3}$$

$[Y]^*$ denotes the total concentration of EDTA not combined with the metal, but including all dissociation forms, which may exist at the particular pH. This $[Y]^*$ may be related to $[Y^{-4}]$ by the formula

$$[Y]^* = [Y^{-4}] \times a_H \tag{4.4}$$

Since $[Y]^*$ is the total concentration of the uncombined EDTA in its various forms, overall balance gives

$$[Y]^* = [Y^{-4}] + [HY^{-3}] + [H_2Y^{-2}] + [H_3Y^{-1}] + [H_4Y] \tag{4.5}$$

Now it is possible to express the various members in equation (4.5) by introducing the acid dissociation constants of EDTA. For practical purposes. however, it is more suitable to use the reciprocal, namely, the "stability constant of the proton complexes" of EDTA. The four expressions are

$$K_1 = \frac{[HY^{-3}]}{[Y^{-4}] \times [H^+]} \tag{4.6a}$$

$$K_2 = \frac{[H_2Y^{-2}]}{[HY^{-3}] \times [H^+]} \tag{4.6b}$$

$$K_3 = \frac{[H_3Y^{-1}]}{[H_2Y^{-2}] \times [H^+]} \tag{4.6c}$$

$$K_4 = \frac{[H_4Y]}{[H_3Y^{-1}] \times [H^+]} \tag{4.6d}$$

Note that the proton stability constants are numbered in reverse order to the corresponding dissociation constants. Thus K_4 as proton stability constant would be K_1 as dissociation constant!

Now $[HY^{-3}]$ may be expressed in terms of $K_1.[H_2Y^{-2}]$ in terms of K_2 and so forth, thus

$$[Y]^* = [Y^{-4}] + K_1 \times [Y^{-4}] \times [H^+] + K_2 \times [HY^{-3}] \times [H^+] +$$
$$+ K_3 \times [H_2Y^{-2}] \times [H^+] + K_4 \times [H_3Y^{-1}] \times [H^+] \qquad (4.7)$$

Substituting further all terms other than $[Y^{-4}]$ by the expressions for the above constants the result is

$$[Y]^* = [Y^{-4}] + K_1 \times [Y^{-4}] \times [H^+] + K_1 \times K_2 \times [Y^{-4}] \times$$
$$[H^+]^2 + K_1 \times K_2 \times K_3 \times [Y^{-4}] \times [H^+]^3 + K_1 \times K_2 \times$$
$$K_3 \times K_4 \times [Y^{-4}] \times [H^+]^4 \qquad (4.8)$$

Combining this equation with (4.4) and dividing by $[Y^{-4}]$ the expression for a_H is obtained

$$a_H = 1 + K_1 \times [H^+] + K_1 \times K_2 \times [H^+]^2 + K_1 \times K_2 \times K_3 \times$$
$$[H^+]^3 + K_1 \times K_2 \times K_3 \times K_4 \times [H^+].^4 \qquad (4.9)$$

This formula allows the calculation of a_H for any pH since the values of the four acidity constants (and therefore their reciprocals) are known (see chapter 2, page 17). A plot of log a_H vs. pH is shown in figure 4. If a_H is known, the apparent stability constant can be calculated by combining (4.2), (4.3) and (4.4)

$$K_{ap. H} = \frac{[MY^{+n-4}]}{[M^{+n}] \times a_H \times [Y^{-4}]} = \frac{K}{a_H} \qquad (4.10a)$$

or

$$\log K_{ap. H} = \log K - \log a_H \qquad (4.10b)$$

Note that this formula contains only the normal complexes MY^{+n-4} and none of the hydrogen (MHY^{+n-3}) or hydroxo complexes ($MOHY^{+n-5}$). Under extreme pH conditions, one or the other of this type of complex may be formed in amounts which cannot be neglected. The expression "extreme pH conditions" is a relative one. For example, for calcium the acid complex forms at pH 4; in contrast, the corresponding iron complex barely exists at a pH higher than 1–2. On the other hand, iron forms a hydroxo complex at a pH of about 7. With calcium the formation of such a complex can be neglected for all practical purposes even at pH value of 12.

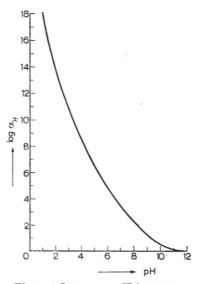

Figure 4. Log a_H vs. pH for EDTA.

(4) Influence of a complex-forming substance other than EDTA.

When another complex-forming substance is present the metal ion is distributed between the complexes formed with this substance and the EDTA. The apparent stability constant which takes into account the influence of this substance, A, is then given by

$$K_{ap. A} = \frac{[MY^{+n-4}]}{[M]^* \times [Y^{-4}]} \tag{4.11}$$

[M]* is now the concentration of the metal ion not combined with EDTA including the "free" metal and also all complexes possibly formed with A. The relation between $[M]^*$ and $[M^{+n}]$ is analogous to that in (4.4) and is given by

$$[M]^* = [M^{+n}] \times \beta_A \qquad (4.12)$$

The complex between M and A is seldom a 1 : 1 complex (e.g. the ammine complexes of copper, zinc, nickel, etc., in ammoniacal solution). Therefore the total amount of the metal ion not combined with EDTA is given as

$$[M]^* = [M^{+n}] + [MA] + [MA_2] + [MA_3] + \ \ldots [MA_m] \quad (4.13)$$

Any charge signs of the A complexes are omitted for the sake of simplicity and because they are not essential. The stability constants of the various complexes between M and A are given by the following equations

$$K_1 = \frac{[MA]}{[M^{+n}] \times [A]} \qquad (4.14a)$$

$$K_2 = \frac{[MA_2]}{[MA] \times [A]} \qquad (4.14b)$$

$$K_m = \frac{[MA_m]}{[MA_{m-1}] \times [A]} \qquad (4.14c)$$

Replacing the terms $[MA]$, $[MA_2]$, $[MA_3]$ $\ldots [MA_m]$ in (4.13) by the appropriate expression derived from the stability constants the following equation results

$$[M]^* = [M^{+n}] + K_1 \times [M^{+n}] \times [A] + K_1 \times K_2 \times [M^{+n}] \times [A]^2 + \\ \ldots K_1 \times K_2 \times K_3 \times \ \ldots K_m \times [M^{+n}] \times [A]^m \quad (4.15)$$

Combination of the last equation with (4.12) gives

$$\beta_A = 1 + K_1 \times [A] + K_1 \times K_2 \times [A]^2 + K_1 \times K_2 \times K_3 \times [A]^3 + \\ \ldots K_1 \times K_2 \times K_3 \times \ \ldots K_m \times [A]^m \quad (4.16)$$

The apparent stability constant is then obtained by combining (4.2), (4.11) and (4.12)

$$K_{\text{ap. A}} = \frac{[MY^{+n-4}]}{[M^{+n}] \times \beta_A \times [Y^{-4}]} = \frac{K}{\beta_A} \qquad (4.17a)$$

or

$$\log K_{\text{ap. A}} = \log K - \log \beta_A \qquad (4.17b)$$

Note that [A] is the concentration of the "free" compound, that is the concentration of A not combined with the metal. Therefore the concentration of total A added is equal to [A] only if a sufficient excess is present so that the relatively small amount combined with the metal may be neglected. Since A is mostly contained in buffers or is added deliberately in excess the condition holds generally closely enough to equate $C_A = [A]$.

(5) The influence of pH *and* another complex-forming substance.

It may happen that both effects mentioned in the preceding sections must be taken into account simultaneously. Then the apparent stability constant can be calculated by combining the two derivations

$$K_{\text{ap. H. A}} = \frac{[MY^{+n-4}]}{[M]^* \times [Y]^*} = \frac{K}{a_H \times \beta_A} \qquad (4.18a)$$

or

$$\log K_{\text{ap. H. A}} = \log K - \log a_H - \log \beta_A \qquad (4.18b)$$

Note that the constants for the complexes between M and A should also be the apparent ones. They can be calculated for the particular pH in a way similar to that given for EDTA.

(6) Other influences.

Most of the stability constants listed in Table 1 (page 25) are measured at $20°$ C and for a medium with the ionic strength $\mu = 0 \cdot 1$. The stability is also influenced by changing these parameters. Increase of ionic strength, i.e., increase of the concentration of neutral salts, decreases the stability. So long as the ionic strength does not exceed $0 \cdot 5$, the effect of such changes on the stability of the complexes may be neglected in practical analysis. However, difficulties may be encountered in solutions containing higher concentrations of neutral salts, especially when a rather weak EDTA complex is involved. Addition of organic solvents (alcohol, acetone, etc.) also increases the stability.

A short but excellent treatment of "constants" is found in reference (1) of the bibliography below.

Bibliography
(1) The analyst and the inconstant constants.
A. Ringbom, *J. Chem. Educat.* **35**, 282 (1958).

CHAPTER 5

EDTA AS A TITRANT (TITRATION CURVES)

IN both the classical acid-base titration and in the EDTA titration a cation is titrated. Hence formal comparison of the two titrations facilitates an understanding of the EDTA titration.

The titration of an acid with a base can be followed graphically by plotting millilitres of base vs. the pH, that is the negative logarithm of the concentration of "free" hydrogen. The titration of a metal with EDTA can similarly be shown graphically by plotting ml EDTA vs. pM, that is the negative logarithm of the concentration of the "free" metal ion. The calculation of the following example may give an idea of this treatment of the problem. Assume 10 ml of a $0 \cdot 01$ M solution of a metal, M, are titrated with $0 \cdot 01$ M EDTA solution, and the stability constant, K, of the metal EDTA complex, MY, formed during the titration has the value 10^{10}. Before any EDTA has been added, the concentration of the metal ion is 10^{-2} and pM is 2. At any phase of the titration between the starting point and very close to the equivalence point the following considerations will serve as a basis for the calculation. The stability of the metal EDTA complex is sufficiently high to neglect the amount of "free" metal ion originating from the dissociation of the metal-EDTA complex. Hence the concentration of "free" metal can be calculated by subtracting the amount complexed with EDTA from the total amount initially present. Thus after 2 ml of EDTA have been added pM is calculated as follows: At the start $0 \cdot 01 \times 10 - 0 \cdot 1$ millimole metal were present. $0 \cdot 01 \times 2 = 0 \cdot 02$ millimole is complexed by the addition of the 2 ml of EDTA. Therefore $0 \cdot 08$ millimole remains uncomplexed. After adding 2 ml of EDTA, the total solution volume is $10 + 2 = 12$ ml. The metal ion concentration is therefore

31

$0 \cdot 08/12 = 6 \cdot 67 \times 10^{-3}$ moles per litre or millimoles per millilitre. pM is then calculated to be $2 \cdot 18$. After 4 ml of EDTA have been added the calculation gives: $(0 \cdot 01 \times 10 - 0 \cdot 01 \times 4)/14 = 4 \cdot 29 \times 10^{-3}$ moles per litre and pM is $2 \cdot 37$. In the same manner other points are calculated until $9 \cdot 9$ or $9 \cdot 99$ ml of EDTA are added.

At the equivalence point the calculation is based on the equation for the stability constant. The analytical (total) concentrations of metal and EDTA are now equal and the total volume is 20 ml. Neglecting the small amount of dissociation, the concentration of the metal-EDTA complex is then $10^{-2}/2 = 5 \times 10^{-3}$. The amount of free metal, [M], equals the amount of free EDTA, [Y]. When these data are introduced into the equation for the stability constants the result is

$$10^{10} = \frac{5 \times 10^{-3}}{[M]^2} \quad \text{and} \quad [M] = \sqrt{5 \times 10^{-13}} = 7 \cdot 07 \times 10^{-7}$$

thus pM is $6 \cdot 15$.

Beyond the endpoint the concentration of the "free" metal ion is calculated as follows: assume 1 ml of EDTA is added in excess. The concentration of free EDTA is therefore $(0 \cdot 01 \times 1)/21 = 4 \cdot 76 \times 10^{-4}$, because the amount of EDTA freed by dissociation of the metal-EDTA complex is so small that it is neglected. The concentration of the metal-EDTA complex can still be considered to be 5×10^{-3}. Introducing these data in the equation of the stability constant we obtain:

$$10^{10} = \frac{5 \times 10^{-3}}{[M] \times 4 \cdot 76 \times 10^{-4}} \quad \text{and } [M] = 1 \cdot 05 \times 10^{-9}$$

and pM is then $8 \cdot 98$.

By plotting the above data point by point, curve C in figure 5 is obtained. Curve B results if $K = 10^6$ and curve D if $K = 10^{16}$.

Obviously the higher the stability of the complex the greater the increase in pM in the endpoint region and the more perpendicular the curve at the equivalence point. The latter is marked on each curve as a cross (see figure 5).

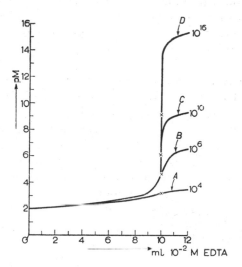

Figure 5. Titration curves. 10 ml 10^{-2} M metal ion solution titrated with 10^{-2} M EDTA. The stability constant of the metal-EDTA complex is written at the particular curve.

The similarity to an acid-base titration with regard to the dissociation constant of the acid being titrated should be noted.

However, one should not forget that this similarity is only a formal one; the EDTA titration is more complicated because there is also a dependence on the pH. To reiterate, EDTA is also an acid and protons can compete with the metal ion for EDTA; therefore close pH control during an EDTA titration is necessary.

For the calculation of any titration curve the apparent stability constant has to be used; this can be calculated using the α_H and β_A factors (see chapter 4, page 30). So long as only the pH influence has to be taken into account the situation is quite simple.

If, however, another complex-forming substance is present the problem is more difficult. If the only information required is the height of the inflection at the equivalence point, the apparent stability constant is simply calculated via the β_A factor, and the titration curve is obtained as above. The quality of the endpoint can then be predicted from the height of the inflection and the slope of the curve at the equivalence point. For a more comprehensive treatment of the problem, however, it has to be taken into consideration that pM is now no longer related to the concentration of the "free" metal ions. The metal ions not complexed by EDTA combine with the other complex-forming substance present. Therefore the titration curve is shifted upwards, parallel to the ordinate and starts at a higher pM depending upon the concentration of the other complex-forming substance and the stability of its metal complexes. For a more detailed treatment of these complicated conditions the comprehensive monograph by Schwarzenbach (listed on page 14) may be consulted.

Bibliography

(1) Chelate complex formation as a basis for titration processes.
G. Schwarzenbach, *Analytica Chimica Acta*, **7**, 141 (1952).
(2) The chelate effect.
G. Schwarzenbach, *Helv. Chim. Acta*, **35**, 2344 (1952) (in German).

CHAPTER 6

ENDPOINT DETECTION IN EDTA TITRATIONS

(1) Visual indications and metal indicators.

The formal similarity mentioned in the preceding chapter between the acid-base and EDTA titrations can be extended to the detection of the endpoint. In an acid-base titration a pH-sensitive indicator is used. At a certain pH range the proton is attached or released depending upon whether the range is approached from a higher or a lower pH. Since the "protonized" form of the indicator differs markedly in colour from the "un-protonized" form, a colour change accompanies the reaction. In an EDTA titration a pM-sensitive indicator is used. At a certain pM range the metal ion is attached or released depending upon whether the range is approached from a higher or lower pM. Since the "metallized" form differs in colour from the "unmetallized" form this reaction is also accompanied by a colour change. In both cases the pH and the pM range respectively must be located at the steepest part of the titration curve and the curve should pass the transformation range as perpendicularly as possible. The ideal condition is obtained when the colour change takes place at the inflection point of the curve, that is, at the pM value of the equivalence point.

Another rather crude qualitative description of the endpoint reaction can be formulated as follows: the metal-indicator complex is weaker than the EDTA complex of the metal being titrated. During the titration the free metal ions are at first progressively complexed with EDTA. Finally the metal is displaced from its indicator complex and transferred to the EDTA, liberating the indicator. Since the free indicator differs in colour from the metallized indicator a colour change occurs.

However, the situation in an EDTA titration is more complicated.

35

pM-sensitive indicators (also called metal indicators or metallochrome indicators), as well as the metal-indicator complex can also
act as acid-base indicators. This is a further reason for maintaining
the pH constant or at least within controlled limits in an EDTA
titration.

Many organic and inorganic substances are known to give colour
reactions with metal ions, but only a limited number can be used
as indicators in EDTA titrations. There are certain requirements to be
fulfilled which include:

(a) The colour reaction must be sensitive so that near the endpoint
when nearly all the metal is bound to the EDTA complex, a
sufficiently strong colour persists in the solution.

(b) The colour reaction should be specific or selective, and subject
to as few interferences as possible.

(c) The colour difference between the metal-indicator complex and
the free indicator must be sufficiently large to be observable by
the human eye.

(d) The metal-indicator complex must be sufficiently stable;
otherwise owing to marked dissociation, a sharp colour change
at the endpoint is not obtained.

(e) The metal-indicator complex must be less stable than the
corresponding metal-EDTA complex, otherwise the EDTA is
unable to remove the metal from the indicator complex at the
endpoint.

(f) The reaction between metal-indicator complex and EDTA
must be sufficiently rapid to permit exact location of the
endpoint. Therefore, in general, only soluble compounds can
be used.

With such information available it is readily appreciated that only
certain types of substances can be used as indicators in EDTA
titrations. Eriochrome Black T and murexide were the first two
introduced by Schwarzenbach and co-workers in the earlier stage
of complexometric titrations. Since that time many investigations
have been made and are still in progress to find new indicators;

a considerable range is now available. It becomes sometimes rather difficult for the beginner to select the proper indicator. Some indicators which represent typical cases are described in chapter 7 (page 38).

One special type of visible indicator may be mentioned apart from the others, namely, fluorescence indicators. These are substances which exhibit fluorescence, preferably under illumination with UV-light. In addition they are also capable of complexing metal ions and upon complexation the fluorescence is quenched. Also the reverse is possible, namely, that the metal complex fluoresces and at the end point of the titration, when the metal is removed from the indicator complex the fluorescence disappears sharply. The overall mechanism of indication, of course, is the same as with the other indicators.

(2) Redox indicators.

As treated in more detail in the theoretical part of chapter 19 (page 113), an EDTA titration may be accompanied by a sudden change in the reduction-oxidation potential of the solution at the endpoint. This change in potential can be indicated visually by a redox-indicator. Only a few practical applications of this indication method exist, at the present time.

(3) Physical methods of endpoint detection.

Instead of using a redox indicator the sudden change in potential at the equivalence point may be indicated by a potentiometer. A theoretical treatment and practical examples of some more important cases for this type of indication are given in chapter 19 (page 113).

If the complex formation is accompanied by a colour change, a photometric titration may be employed or an indicator may be added and the colour change at the endpoint followed photometrically. Theoretical considerations and experiments are given in chapter 21 (page 125).

Other changes of physical properties can be used for an endpoint detection in an EDTA titration including height of the diffusion current (amperometric titration), temperature change due to heat of reaction of the complex reaction (thermometric titration), and change of conductivity in the solution (conductometric titration). However it is unnecessary for an introductory course to go into details of such procedures.

CHAPTER 7

SOME IMPORTANT METAL INDICATORS

(1) Eriochrome Black T (Erio T) and Calmagite.

Eriochrome Black T, in the present booklet always abbreviated as Erio T, is an azo dye of the following structure:

It is commercially available as the sodium salt under various dye trade names according to the particular firm which markets it: Solochrome Black T, TS and WDFA, Chromogen Black T, Chrome T, Pontachrome Black TA, etc. The colour index number is C.I. 203.

The substance is a water-soluble black powder with a metallic lustre.

Prepare a 0·1 per cent aqueous solution of the compound. The solution is not stable for a long time and must be renewed after 1–2 weeks, depending on the purity, storage conditions, etc. Heavy metals, especially copper and iron, seem to catalyse the decomposition. For titration purposes it is preferable to use a solid mixture with an inert substance (see chapter 12, page 69). The solution only should be used for the experiments described in this chapter, to facilitate the addition of equal amounts in experiments where comparisons are made.

In practice Erio T is being replaced by Calmagite which is also an o, o'–azo dye. Its formula is

It can be used in every respect like Erio T. Colour changes and stability constants of the Ca and Mg complexes are for all practical purposes identical. The advantage of Calmagite is its stability on storage. Instead of a solid dilution, a 0·1% solution in water containing a few drops of buffer pH 10 may be used. The solution is practically stable indefinitely. All experiments and facts described in the following paragraphs for Erio T are equally pertinent for Calmagite.

(1.a) Acid—base properties.

The sulphonic group in Erio T can be assumed to be completely dissociated within the acidity range of EDTA titrations so that the dye anion may be written as H_2F^-. According to the pH the remaining two (phenolic) hydrogen ions are more or less dissociated and their dissociation is accompanied by colour changes.

Experiment 7.1: Place 4 drops of indicator solution in a test tube and wash down with 5 ml of water. Add 1 drop of 0·1 M EDTA to counteract the effect of any metal impurities present. Add 1 drop of 0·1 M hydrochloric acid and observe the deep red solution colour. Add dropwise 0·1 M sodium hydroxide; note that the colour turns to blue. Add 1 drop of 2 N sodium hydroxide and the red colour reappears. Save this solution for experiment 7.2.

The reaction scheme for the above experiment may be written as:

$$H_2F^- \underset{+H^+}{\overset{-H^+}{\rightleftarrows}} HF^{-2} \underset{+H^+}{\overset{-H^+}{\rightleftarrows}} F^{-3} \qquad (7.1)$$

$$\text{red} \leftarrow \text{pH } 6 \rightarrow \text{blue} \leftarrow \text{pH } 12 \rightarrow \text{orange}$$

(1.b) Erio T as metallochrome indicator.

According to the pH of the solution Erio T can occur in three differently coloured forms. If Erio T is used as indicator in an EDTA titration only the blue form is of interest. This blue colour changes to red if complex formation with a metal ion takes place. In some cases this reaction is rapidly and readily reversed by addition of EDTA; in others the reaction is slow and/or not reversible.

Experiment 7.2: Take the solution left from experiment 7.1 and add 5 drops of buffer pH 10 solution. The blue colour is restored. Then add 2 drops of $0 \cdot 1$ M magnesium ion solution and observe the wine-red colour of the magnesium-Erio T complex. Add dropwise $0 \cdot 1$ M EDTA; the blue colour reappears because the magnesium forms a stronger complex with the EDTA than with Erio T.

The reaction may be written as

$$Mg^{+2} + HF^{-2} \underset{\leftarrow}{\overset{\rightarrow}{}} MgF^{-1} + H^+ \tag{7.2}$$

The sensitivity of this colour reaction is outstanding. Schwarzenbach has shown that under proper conditions even 10^{-7} to 10^{-8} M magnesium ion solution and somewhat more concentrated calcium ion solutions give a faintly but nevertheless visible red tint with Erio T.

The release of calcium and/or magnesium from the glass of containers can be easily demonstrated using this highly sensitive reaction.

Experiment 7.3: Take a soft-glass container (preferably an unused one) and rinse it thoroughly with redistilled water. Place redistilled water in it and add 1 ml of buffer pH 10 solution and 2 drops of indicator. The solution should develop a blue colour. If not, add dropwise an EDTA solution obtained by diluting 1 drop of $0 \cdot 1$ M EDTA with 5 ml of water, until the blue colour just shows. Now allow to stand for a short time and observe the reappearance of the red colour caused by the release of calcium from the glass. This red colour can be removed by addition of a few more drops of diluted EDTA; the red colour will return yet again. The process can be repeated several times. Take a glass rod and scratch the inside wall of the container; the reappearance of the red colour is extremely rapid. The scratched surface delivers large quantities of ions.

The conclusion of this very impressive experiment should always be remembered in analyses employing EDTA. Even borosilicate containers, especially when factory-new, show this behaviour to a certain extent. The amount of metal ions released is smaller and the rate is lower, but nevertheless not negligible over a long period. This is especially true with regard to analyses where dilute solutions are used.

(1.c) Blocking of the indicator.

Metal ions other than calcium and magnesium also form red coloured Erio T complexes; but not all complexes are deprived of the metal by addition of EDTA or the blue colour is so slowly restored that the colour change is unsuited to indicator use.

Repeat experiment 7.2 using, instead of the magnesium solution, individual solutions of calcium, zinc, nickel, cobalt, lead, or iron (III). In order to avoid precipitation of hydroxides add 2 drops of 1 M sodium tartrate solution in the case of lead and iron. Note the colour changes; note that the colours are red but of different shade and note which of the indicator complexes are decomposed by addition of EDTA. Some additional very important cases are described below.

(1.d) Action of aluminium.

Experiment 7.4: Place 1 drop of 0·1 M aluminium solution, 1 drop of 1 M sodium tartrate and 5 drops of buffer pH 10 in a test-tube and dilute to about 5 ml. Add 4 drops of indicator solution and note the slow appearance of the red colour. Add dropwise EDTA and note that even with a great excess of EDTA and a long waiting time, the blue does not reappear. The indicator is blocked.

The strong complex formed between aluminium and Erio T prevents the possibility of a (direct) titration of aluminium with EDTA. Because of this blocking of the indicator the titration of any other metal is impossible in presence of aluminium, unless this reaction is prevented by addition of a masking reagent (see chapter 9, page 55).

(1.e) Action of copper.

Copper can be considered as a "poison" for Erio T and for many other indicators of similar structure; this can be demonstrated by the following series of experiments.

Experiment 7.5: Maintain the order of additions in this experiment strictly as given! Place six test-tubes in a rack and place 1 drop of 0·1 M copper solution in each tube. Then add 3 drops of buffer pH 10 to each tube and add EDTA according to the table below. Roman numbers indicate the number of the tube. Arabic numbers show the number of drops of 0·1 M EDTA to be added.

I 0,   II 2,   III 2,   IV 10,   V 0,   VI 0

Wash the walls of the tubes down with about 5 ml of water. Now place in each tube 4 drops of indicator and shake well. Note that the solutions in tubes I, V and VI are now red, and that tubes II and III gradually become reddish after some time. The delay depends somewhat on temperature and also drop-size delivered from the different droppers. The solution in tube IV remains blue.

Add 10 drops of 0·1 M EDTA to tube I, shake and observe the slow and gradual change of red to blue. Add 8 drops more of EDTA to tube III; note that the solution also becomes blue after some time.

The stability constants of the copper-Erio T and the copper-EDTA complex are not very dissimilar. Hence copper will shift from one complex to the other according to the concentration of the complex-forming reagent. The rates of the reactions, however, are very slow. Therefore the indicator is blocked even by traces of copper.

To exclude the action of copper, it can be transformed into the very stable (and therefore inactive) copper(I)-cyano complex by reaction with potassium cyanide. The course of this reaction is very interesting.

Add to tube V one drop of 5 per cent potassium cyanide solution. The solution colour turns to yellow. Allow the tube to stand for some time; the blue colour of free Erio T slowly appears.

Copper is transformed to the cyano complex according to the reaction

$$2Cu(NH_3)_4^{+2} + 10CN^- \longrightarrow 2Cu(CN)_4^{-3} + C_2N_2 + 8NH_3 \quad (7\cdot3)$$

During the reduction the redox potential is raised considerably and the dye is probably oxidized to a yellow form which is inactive as a metal indicator. (For a more comprehensive treatment of the relation between redox potential and complex formation see chapter 19 (page 113).) This oxidation of the dye is reversible, but only slowly and in most cases not completely. The blue developed is not pure and obviously some of the dye is irreversibly decomposed.

When a reducing reagent is present during the formation of the copper(I)-cyano complex the oxidation of the dye is prevented and the blue colour is obtained immediately.

Take tube VI and add a few crystals of ascorbic acid, and then one drop of 5 per cent potassium cyanide solution and shake. The blue colour of the free indicator appears at once.

(1.f.) Action of manganese.

Experiment 7.6: Place three test-tubes in a rack and add to each tube 5 drops of 0·1 M manganese(II) solution and wash down with 5 ml of water. Add a few crystals of ascorbic acid to tube III and add 3 drops buffer pH 10 to tube II. Place in each tube 4 drops of Erio T indicator solution. Now add to tube I and III, 4 drops of buffer pH 10. Shake the three tubes vigorously, so that some air is absorbed by each of the solutions.

Tubes I and II, either immediately or after a short time, become dirty orange or yellow owing to the oxidation of manganese(II) in ammoniacal solution to manganese(IV) which blocks the indicator. The formation is independent of the order of addition of the reagents (tubes I and II). Add EDTA to tube I and note that the colour does not change to blue even after a considerable time. Now add a few crystals of ascorbic acid to tube I and at once the blue appears. Manganese in its higher state of valence is reduced to manganese(II) which is complexed with EDTA so that the indicator appears in its free form. Add ascorbic acid to tube II and the red colour of the manganese(II)-Erio T complex will appear. Add EDTA and the colour changes from red to blue. Therefore in presence of manganese a reducing reagent should be added to eliminate difficulties caused by oxidation effects.

(1.g) Action of nickel.

Experiment 7.7: Place 1 drop of 0·1 M nickel solution, 3 drops of buffer pH 10 and 4 drops of indicator in a test-tube and dilute with 5 ml of water. The solution colour is red. Add EDTA dropwise; note that the indicator is blocked by nickel; add 1 drop of 5 per cent potassium cyanide and immediately the colour changes to blue owing to the masking of nickel by its transformation to the very stable tetracyano complex.

Experiment 7.8: Place 1 drop of 0·1 M nickel solution, 2 drops of 0·1 M EDTA and 3 drops of buffer pH 10 in a test-tube. Dilute to 5 ml with water. Now (follow exactly the order given for the additions) add 4 drops of indicator solution. The colour of the solution is blue and remains so for an appreciable time. Do not wait until the blue changes, but add 0·1 M magnesium dropwise until the red of the magnesium-Erio T complex appears. Again add EDTA and the blue is restored. This colour change of red-blue-red can be repeated once or twice more if one works quickly. Add magnesium in excess, allow to stand for some minutes and again add EDTA. The red solution colour persists; the indicator is blocked!

In experiment 7.7 the strong nickel-Erio T complex was formed and EDTA was unable to withdraw the nickel from it. In experiment 7.8 the EDTA complex of nickel was formed before the addition of the indicator. Nickel is known to be very slow in most of its complexing reactions. The exchange reaction between the Erio T and the EDTA complex of the nickel is sufficiently slow for the magnesium-Erio T endpoint to be obtained repeatedly before enough nickel is released to block the indicator. If, however, the solution is allowed to stand in contact with excess of free magnesium the replacement reaction is forced and blocking occurs more quickly.

For a practical application of this finding see the determination of nickel according to experiment 15.3, page 91.

The action of the metals studied in this chapter are typical cases. Other metal ions react in a similar way and other azo-dyes behave very much like Erio T. The understanding of these reactions is extremely important for an appropriate selection of the titration conditions.

Bibliography on Erio T and similar dyes.

(1) The alkaline earth complexes of *o,o'*–dihydroxy azo dyes.
G. Schwarzenbach and W. Biedermann, *Helv. Chim. Acta*, **31**, 678 (1948) (in German).

(2) Some *o,o'*–dihydroxy azo indicator dyes for EDTA titrations.
R. Belcher, R. A. Close and T. S. West, *Chemist Analyst* **46**, 86 (1957) and **47**, 2 (1958).

(3) Indicator for the titration of calcium and magnesium with EDTA.
F. Lindstrom and H. Diehl, *Anal. Chem.* **32**, 1123 (1960).

(2) Murexide.

Murexide is the ammonium salt of purpuric acid of the formula

$$NH—C—O^- \qquad O=C—NH$$
$$O=C \qquad C—N=C \qquad C=O$$
$$NH—C=O \qquad O=C—NH$$

and forms coloured complexes with many metal ions. The colour of the unmetallized murexide in ammoniacal or soda-alkaline solution is deep violet

Murexide solutions are only stable for a day or so and must be prepared freshly every day. A solution should be used only for the experiments in this section. For titration purposes a "solid dilution" is preferable (see page 76). Prepare a solution as follows. Place a spatula-end of murexide into a test-tube and add 5 ml of water. Let stand for about 10 minutes with occasional shaking. If all the powder dissolves add more and shake again. If some murexide remains undissolved after 3–5 minutes the solution may be considered saturated. Filter off or decant the dark coloured liquid and store it in a dropping bottle. Use the liquid on the day of preparation and for the experiments in this section only.

Experiment 7.9: Place 1 drop of 0·1 M calcium solution in a test-tube and dilute with 5 ml of water. Add 2 drops of 6 N sodium hydroxide and 2 drops of murexide solution. Note the salmon red colour of the calcium murexide complex. Add 2 drops of 0·1 M EDTA. Note the colour changes to violet, the colour of the free murexide. Add the sodium hydroxide only after dilution of the test solution with water, otherwise precipitation of calcium carbonate or hydroxide may occur. These salts will dissolve only slowly; they do react with EDTA but at a low rate.

Experiment 7.10: Place 1 drop of 0·1 M nickel solution, 1 drop of buffer pH 10 and 2 drops of murexide solution in a test-tube. Dilute with 5 ml of water. Note the yellow colour of the nickel murexide complex. Add 2 drops of 0·1 M EDTA. Note the colour changes to violet.

Experiment 7.11: Place in a test-tube 1 drop of 0·1 M copper solution, 1 drop of buffer pH 10, 2 drops of murexide solution and dilute with 3 ml of water. The solution is yellow owing to the colour of the copper-murexide complex. The yellow may have a little greenish tint owing to the presence of the blue copper-tetrammine complex. Add 2 drops of 0·1 M EDTA and the colour turns to violet. Now add 2 further drops of copper solution; the yellow colour is restored. Add 5 drops of buffer pH 10 and the solution becomes violet. The copper-tetrammine complex is sufficiently strong to remove the copper from the murexide complex if the ammonia concentration becomes high. This is important in a titration. Always keep the ammonia concentration sufficiently low to ensure a sharp endpoint. Dilute the violet solution with water until the test-tube is nearly full. The ammonia concentration thereby decreases and the yellow colour returns. The latter part of the experiment is a nice demonstration of the superiority of the 1 : 1 Cu-Murexide complex over the 1 : 4 Cu-tetrammine complex.

Experiment 7.12: Place 1–2 drops of murexide solution and 1 drop of buffer pH 10 in a test-tube and dilute with 3 ml of water. Add dropwise 0·1 M magnesium solution and note the slow delayed change from violet to orange. Murexide forms with magnesium a complex that is too weak to permit its use as an indicator in the titration of magnesium. Now add 2 drops of 6 N sodium hydroxide; the colour changes to violet. Magnesium is precipitated as the hydroxide and the indicator is released. Add 1 drop of 0·1 M calcium solution; the colour of the calcium-murexide complex appears. This is the basis for the determination of calcium in presence of magnesium (experiment 18.4, page 105).

Some metals other than those mentioned in the preceding experiments also give coloured complexes with murexide. Conduct experiments in the same way as for nickel (experiment 7.10) using lead, manganese, zinc, cobalt, iron (III) and observe the colour changes, if any. In the cases of lead and iron add some tartrate ion to prevent precipitation. Observe that the colours obtained with cobalt are dependent on pH.

Keep the murexide solution and repeat experiment 7.10 during several days with the ageing indicator solution; note its rapid decomposition. Note that after a few days the colour change becomes so indistinct that it cannot be used for the detection of the endpoint in a titration.

(3) PAN

PAN is the abbreviation for 1-(2-pyridylazo)-2-naphthol of the structure

The brick-red substance is insoluble in water, but dissolves in. alkali, ammonia and organic solvents. The solution in methanol or ethanol is stable indefinitely.

The acid-base properties of PAN are not as pronounced as those of Erio T or some other indicators. Only a slight colour change from yellow to orange can be noted at pH about 8–9.

The metal complexes of PAN are also insoluble in water; hence the reaction with EDTA is very slow. Accordingly, the titration should be done in boiling solution or in a medium 50 per cent in ethanol or acetone. This is particularly effective for copper which is the most important metal for which PAN serves as indicator.

The colour reaction between copper and PAN is very sensitive, but many other metals, including nickel, cobalt, zinc, lead, bismuth and cadmium give coloured complexes with PAN. Of these metals only a few can be titrated *directly*, because of the slow reaction or the low colour sensitivity. The nickel-PAN complex especially reacts so slowly with EDTA that a titration is practically impossible; the indicator is almost blocked by nickel.

Experiment 7.13: Place 1 drop of 0·1 M copper solution, 2 drops of buffer pH 5, and 2 drops of 0·05 per cent ethanolic PAN solution in a test-tube. Note the formation of the insoluble, violet copper-PAN complex. Dilute with 5 ml of water. Add 2 drops of 0·1 M EDTA and note the slow colour change from violet to yellow. Repeat the experiment but add the EDTA to the boiling test solution. Finally repeat the experiment but add only 3 ml of water and a further 3 ml of ethanol. Note the quick reaction in the last two experiments.

Experiment 7.14: Place 1 drop of 0·1 M nickel solution, 3 drops of buffer pH 5 and 2 drops of 0·05 per cent ethanolic PAN solution in a test-tube and dilute with 2 ml of water. Note the slight turbidity caused by the insoluble nickel-PAN complex. Add 2 ml of ethanol and note that the precipitate dissolves. Add 3 drops of 0·1 M EDTA. Even after prolonged standing, the colour does not change. Heat to boiling and note the slow change to yellow or sometimes (depending on the concentrations of the reactants) to an incomplete colour change (orange).

Repeat the experiment in the same manner with zinc, cobalt, lead, iron(III); compare the intensities of the developed colours (if any) with that of the copper-PAN complex and note further the rapidity of the colour change (if any) after addition of EDTA.

Bibliography on PAN and its application.
   (1) 1-(2-pyridylazo)-2-naphthol as a possible analytical reagent. R. L. Cheng and R. H. Bray, *Analyt. Chem.*, **27**, 782 (1955).
   (2) Complexometric micro-titrations using PAN as indicator. H. Flaschka and H. Abdine, *Chemist Analyst*, **45**, 2 (1956).

(4) Pyrocatechol Violet.

The formula of this indicator is

The indicator has acid-base properties and the colour of its solution changes with the pH. At a pH below 1·5 the colour is red. Between pH 2 and 6 the colour is pure yellow. At a pH above 6 the colour turns to violet, and above pH 9 more of the phenolic groups dissociate accompanied by a colour change to purple.

Experiment 7.15: Place 2 drops of 0·1 per cent Pyrocatechol Violet in a test-tube and dilute with 5 ml of water. Add 1 drop of 2 N sulphuric acid and note the colour changes to red. Add 1 drop of 0.1 M EDTA to avoid any interference by metals which may form coloured complexes with the indicator and which might be present in trace amounts. Now add 2 N sodium hydroxide solution dropwise and observe the colour changes indicated above.

Although an aqueous solution of Pyrocatechol Violet is stable for a long period, the indicator is rapidly decomposed by atmospheric oxidation at higher pH values. This may be prevented by the addition of ascorbic acid.

Experiment 7.16: Take two test-tubes and place 2 drops of 0·1 per cent Pyrocatechol Violet in each. To one of the tubes add a few crystals of ascorbic acid. Then place in both tubes 5 drops of buffer pH 10 and dilute with 5 ml of water. Place both tubes in a rack and observe the fading of the colour in the tube to which no ascorbic acid had been added.

Pyrocatechol Violet forms blue coloured complexes in acid medium as well as in ammoniacal medium with many metal ions. For practical purposes the most important metal seems to be bismuth, which can be titrated very selectively in a strongly acidic medium.

The colour change in acid medium from blue to yellow is very sharp. A special phenomenon occurs with the bismuth complex.

Experiment 7.17: Place one drop of 0·1 M bismuth solution and 3 drops of 0·1 per cent Pyrocatechol Violet solution in a test-tube and dilute with 5 ml of water. The solution has the correct pH of about 2–3 and the colour of the solution is a deep cornflower blue. Now add 0·01 M EDTA solution dropwise and shake after each addition. Before the final yellow appears the solution becomes red. This is due to change in the ratio Bi : dye. So long as bismuth is in excess the blue 2 : 1 complex exists. When approaching the end point the concentration of free bismuth becomes progressively smaller and eventually close to that of the indicator, so that only the red 1 : 1 complex can be formed. Because the indicator concentration is small, it may be difficult to establish the red colour. To bring it out clearly titrate either with a more dilute EDTA solution or even better use 10–12 or more drops of indicator. .

The appearance of the red colour (at least in the vicinity of the added drop of EDTA) during a titration serves as a warning that the endpoint is near.

The colour change in ammoniacal solution is rather poor, because it is difficult to distinguish between violet and blue. The endpoint under such conditions is inferior to that of Erio T. However, one advantage of Pyrocatechol Violet is that it is not blocked by copper, nickel, cobalt and some other heavy metals as is Erio T. Conduct experiments similar to experiment 7.2, page 40, using Pyrocatechol Violet instead of Erio T with various metals. Note the colour changes. Remember that in ammoniacal solution the colour of the free Pyrocatechol Violet is violet and that of the metallized indicator is blue, in contrast to Erio T.

Bibliography
(1) Pyrocatechol Violet: indicator for the EDTA titration.
V. Suk and M. Malat, *Chemist Analyst*, **45**, 30, 61 (1956).

(5) Xylenol Orange (XO)

Xylenol Orange, conveniently abbreviated XO, is a red to brown powder readily soluble in water. The formula of XO is

The substance is synthesized by introducing, via a Mannich reaction, the iminodiacetic acid groups into *o*-cresolsulphophthaleine which is known as Cresol Red and used as an acid base indicator. Many valuable metal indicators have been obtained by introducing the complexing group (which is also part of the EDTA molecule!!) into acid base indicators and other substances.

The acid-base indicator properties of the parent substance is still found in XO, which is yellow in acidic medium and changes colour beginning at about pH 6 to a brilliant violet. Most of the metal complexes are red or violet so that the application of XO as a metal indicator is restricted to solutions with a pH below 6; then the end point in a complexometric titration is from red or violet to lemon yellow. Complex formation with some metal occurs even in extremely acid solution. Zirconium can be titrated in 1 N and bismuth in 0·5 N nitric acid. The titration of these and some other metals of higher valency is done with excellent selectivity, because at so high an acidity many of the divalent metals do not react with the indicator and EDTA

Experiment 7.18: Place 3 drops of a 0·1% XO solution and 1 drop of 1 : 2 nitric acid into a test tube and dilute with 5 ml of water. Add dropwise 2 N NaOH and observe the colour change to violet. Keep the tube for the purpose of comparing colours.

Experiment 7.19: Place 3 drops of a 0·1 M lead solution, 2 drops of buffer pH 5 and 3 drops of 0·1% XO into a test-tube. Dilute with 5 ml of water and observe the red colour of the Pb-XO complex. Compare with the colour of the alkaline form of XO; it will be obvious why XO can hardly be used as indicator above pH 6. Add dropwise EDTA and note the sharp colour change to lemon yellow.

Repeat this experiment but use other metal ions such as Zn, Hg, Cd Ni, Co, Mn, etc., and note the colours, if any, and reaction upon addition of EDTA. Find out what happens when Fe(III) is examined at pH 2–3.

Experiment 7.20: Place 1 drop of 1 : 2 nitric acid and 3 drops of 0·1% XO into a test tube and dilute with 5 ml of water. Add 1 drop of 0·1 M bismuth solution and observe the red colour of the Bi-XO complex. Add dropwise 0·1 M EDTA and notice the change to lemon yellow. Now add 2–3 drops of 0·1 M lead solution. No colour change takes place because at the low pH the Pb-XO complex does not form. Increase the pH by adding dropwise buffer pH 5; the colour changes to the red of the lead-indicator complex. Add 0·1 M EDTA and again the yellow of the free indicator appears. Thus not only can bismuth be titrated in presence of lead but also the consecutive determination of the two metals is possible (see experiment 18.1).

Bibliography
(1) Xylenol Orange: A new indicator for the EDTA titration.
J. Körbl and R. Pribil, *Chemist-Analyst* **45**, 102 (1956).

CHAPTER 8

SELECTIVITY OF EDTA TITRATIONS

As pointed out in chapter 1 (page 13), EDTA forms stable complexes with nearly all polyvalent metal cations. So far the EDTA titration has been applied to the determination of about thirty common metals. Further, all rare earths and some actinides can be titrated. This refers only to the application of direct or back-titration procedures. There are some additional metal ions and also anions which can be titrated by indirect methods. This demonstrates quite clearly that the selectivity of EDTA titrations is very low.

Nevertheless, there are some means by which the selectivity can be enhanced. Under favourable conditions it is possible to determine up to three metals in successive titrations in the same solution. When aliquot portions are used, up to five constituents may be determined in the same sample without the need of prior separation (see experiment 18.6, page 108).

It is obvious that one metal can be titrated in the presence of another only when their stability constants are sufficiently different. The question then arises: how much must this difference be?

Assume two metals, M and N, are present in the same solution; M is to be titrated and the endpoint is to be indicated by any means *except* by use of a complex-forming indicator. At the endpoint the two metals compete for the EDTA according to the equilibrium

$$NY + M \rightleftarrows N + MY \qquad (8.1)$$

The equilibrium constant of this reaction is given by

$$K_{equ.} = \frac{[N] \times [MY]}{[NY] \times [M]} \qquad (8.2)$$

When the right side is multiplied by $[Y]/[Y]$ it becomes obvious that it is the ratio of the stability constants of the two metal complexes and one obtains

$$K_{equ.} = \frac{K_M}{K_N} \qquad (8.3)$$

In order that the equilibrium (8:1) at the end point of the titration of M is shifted desirably far to the right side, a high value of $K_{equ.}$ is necessary which can only be secured when K_M is sufficiently greater than K_N. For a general evaluation of the situation the same thumb rule as in acid-base titrations may be invoked, namely that the ratio of the two constants should be about 10^4 or greater. The exact value, of course, depends on the concentration ratio of the two metal ions, the precision with which the end point can be located and the error which is considered to be permissible in the titration. Needless to say the apparent stability constant of the metal to be titrated (M) must have a value of at least 10^6 or 10^7, which value was already established previously as a minimum for a titration to be feasible at all.

The situation becomes entirely different when a complex-forming indicator is involved. Let us assume there are again two metals, M and N, present in the solution. If the indicator reacts with both metal ions, quite obviously, only the sum of the metals can be obtained by a titration. Hence, a selective indicator is needed. Let us assume the indicator reacts with metal M only. Then for a selective titration of M it is required that M forms the more stable complex as above. The equilibrium at the end point may now be described by

$$NY + MI \rightleftarrows MY + N + I \qquad (8.4)$$

where I stands for the indicator ion. The equilibrium constant for this reaction is analogously expressed as in the simplest case discussed above and the expression takes the form

$$K_{equ.} = \frac{[MY] \times [N] \times [I]}{[NY] \times [MI]} = \frac{K_M}{K_N \times K_{MI}} \qquad (8.5)$$

The right-side term is readily obtained by multiplying the middle term by $[M] \times [Y]/[M] \times [Y]$ and introducing the appropriate stability constants, which also here, of course, are the apparent ones.

Upon inspection of (8.5) it can readily be deduced that a factor 10^4 for K_M/K_N is inadequate and that it must be increased for the stability of the indicator complex. Hence, an indicator which has a metal complex of low stability is desirable for selective titration. But the stability cannot be so low that difficulties arise owing to extensive dissociation of the indicator complex around the end point. Also here, the exact data will depend upon the concentrations of the species involved, the error permissible, etc.

It has been expressed repeatedly that the apparent stability constants have to be used, which can be obtained via the α_H and β_A factors. Because the α_H factor is related to the EDTA itself, it is the same for both metal ions and will cancel out. Hence, not too much influence can be expected in this direction unless the metal with the lower stability of its EDTA complex (N) is at the titration-pH practically completely dissociated, whereas the metal to be titrated still forms a complex of reasonably high apparent stability. For example, at pH-values lower than about 4–5, alkaline earths and magnesium do not interfere with the titration of other metals (except manganese), even if a complex forming indicator is employed. For a theoretical treatment of this situation, however, expanded and more complicated formulae are necessary.

Greater selectivity can be obtained by variation of the ratio of the constants via the β_A factor. Suppose two metals, M and N, are considered. N forms a very stable complex with another complexforming substance, A, whereas M does not react with that substance. Then the apparent stability constant of N will become considerably lower (via a high β_A factor) than that of M, and the selective titration of M becomes possible even if the absolute constant K_N is higher than K_M. For example this condition holds when magnesium is titrated in the presence of iron, and the latter is transformed to the very stable hexacyano-complex. For a more detailed treatment of such possibilities of masking see chapter 9 (page 55).

A few cases exist where selectivity can be achieved through marked difference in the rate of reaction. The formation of the chromium(III)-EDTA complex at room temperature is so extremely slow (see experiment 3.4, page 20) that other metals can be titrated in its presence, and the titration is finished before any appreciable amount of chromium-EDTA complex is formed. This, in spite of the high stability constant of the chromium-EDTA complex (log $K=23$!).

A decrease in the rate of reaction may be obtained deliberately by cooling the solution. Nickel at $0°$ C and pH about 2 is removed by bismuth from its EDTA complex only extremely slowly. If equimolar amounts of nickel-EDTA complex and bismuth nitrate solutions are mixed and cooled, only about 1 per cent of the nickel is replaced within half an hour. Under the same conditions cobalt and certain other metals are replaced almost instantaneously. This allows a selective determination of nickel in the presence of other metals (especially cobalt), by employing a back-titration with bismuth.

CHAPTER 9

MASKING

As pointed out in the preceding chapter, the differences in general between the stability constants of the various metals are not sufficiently marked to permit a sufficient selectivity in titrations with EDTA. Hence, some measures have to be taken to eliminate the action of interfering metals on EDTA. This is done by *masking*, which can be defined in general terms as follows: *masking* is the prevention of the reaction of one substance with another substance without physical separation. Reagents which have this effect are called *masking reagents*, Sometimes the term "screening" is used; but we shall reserve this expression for the addition of a dye to sharpen the colour change of an indicator. The prevention of the action of a masking reagent by a further reagent is called *demasking*.

Masking may be effected by one or more of the following means.

(1) pH-adjustment.

Lowering the pH may cause the EDTA complex of a very weakly combined metal to dissociate completely. Then another metal which has a highly stable EDTA complex can be titrated, see chapter 8 (page 51). The H^+-ion can be considered to be a masking reagent, according to the broadest meaning of the definition.

(2) Complex formation.

If a solution of two metals is treated with a reagent which forms a stable complex with one and a very weak or no complex with the other metal, it is possible to increase sufficiently the difference of the two apparent stability constants of the metal-EDTA complexes to effect a selective titration.

Zinc, copper, nickel, cobalt and some other metals form very stable cyano complexes. In contrast, the corresponding complex of lead or manganese is very weak, whereas calcium and magnesium do not form cyano-complexes at all. Accordingly, the latter metals can be titrated when the former are masked by addition of potassium cyanide. The cyano-complexes are so stable that zinc, copper, etc. are virtually removed completely from their EDTA complexes.

Zinc can be demasked selectively from its cyano complex by addition of formaldehyde (experiment 18.2, page 102).

Triethanolamine forms a stable complex with aluminium (and some other metal ions) and is mainly used to eliminate the action of aluminium. Aluminium in strong alkaline medium is also masked by hydroxyl ions, inasmuch as it is transformed into the aluminate ion, a process which can also be considered as complex formation.

The complex HgI_4^{-2} is very stable; hence potassium iodide can be used for a highly selective masking of mercuric ion.

There are other complex-forming substances known which are used as masking reagents. For a more comprehensive list one of the books listed on pages 14 and 15 should be consulted.

(3) Precipitation.

The solubility products of some precipitates are so low that precipitation occurs even in presence of EDTA. On the other hand, when a precipitate is formed it may not redissolve in EDTA, or the resolution may be so slow that another metal can be titrated before any appreciable amount is dissolved. This effect can also be applied for masking purposes.

For example, magnesium can be titrated in presence of calcium, if the latter has been precipitated with oxalate. Magnesium can be titrated in the presence of barium if the latter has been precipitated with sulphate or, better, chromate. Calcium can be titrated in presence of magnesium if the latter is precipitated as hydroxide (see experiment 18.4, page 105).

However, it is important to titrate in the presence of the precipitate for the process to be quoted as an example of masking. If the precipitate is filtered off it is no longer masking but separation.

Aluminium, calcium and magnesium can be precipitated with fluoride; bismuth can be masked by hydrolysing with a chloride-containing solution so that the sparingly soluble bismuth oxychloride is formed.

It may seem that many precipitating reactions could be used for masking purposes, but this approach is relatively limited. Precipitation reactions are in most cases affected by occlusion, co- and post-precipitation, adsorption and other phenomena which cause serious trouble; furthermore, the colour change of an indicator can be obscured by the presence of a precipitate. Hence, whenever possible, complex formation is to be preferred.

(4) Oxidation and reduction.

Oxidation or reduction may convert a metal ion to a state where a weaker EDTA complex or no complex at all is formed. Iron(III) can be reduced to iron(II) by addition of ascorbic acid in slightly acid medium. The stability constant of the EDTA complex of iron (II) is about eleven log K units lower than that of iron(III), thus the interference due to iron can be eliminated when titration is done in acid medium. Ascorbic acid reduces mercury(II) to metal which does not interfere. Chromium(III) can be oxidized to chromate with hydrogen peroxide in alkaline solution. Chromate as an anion does not form an EDTA complex and the interference is eliminated.

At the present time a great number of masking reagents is known that act according to the various principles mentioned above. Of course, in a multi-component mixture a single masking reagent may not be enough and several then have to be applied.

It should be noted that masking is not only applied to avoid interferences caused by reaction of EDTA with associated metals. Even trace amounts, which would not alter the result of the titration if co-titrated, could interfere seriously and even make a titration impossible. For example, many indicators are blocked by traces of copper; this effect may be overcome by addition of an appropriate masking reagent. It may be further noted that EDTA itself sometimes acts as masking reagent to protect an indicator if a back-titration procedure is applied; any interfering metal is then complexed and its interference is prevented.

Bibliography on masking.

(1) Masking of aluminium, iron and manganese. (Triethanolamine)
R. Pribil, *Coll. Czechosl. Chem. Commun.* **19,** 58 (1954) and also p. 465.

(2) Masking of aluminium, magnesium and calcium with ammonium fluoride.
R. Pribil, *Coll. Czechosl. Chem. Commun.* **19,** 64 (1954) (in German).

(3) Masking of cations with 2,3-dimercaptopropanol.
R. Pribil and Z. Roubal, *Coll. Czechosl. Chem. Commun.* **19,** 1162 (1954) (in German).

(4) The specific determination of zinc and cadmium in presence of other metals (demasking with formaldehyde).
H. Flaschka, *Z. anal. Chem.* **138,** 332 (1953) (in German).

(5) Volumetric determination of zinc in metallurgical products by use of disodium EDTA. (demasking with formaldehyde).
J. Kinnunen and B. Merikanto, *Chemist Analyst,* **41.**76 (1952).

(6) Increasing selectivity of analytical reactions by masking.
K. L. Cheng, *Anal. Chem.* **33,** 783 (1961).

CHAPTER 10

TYPES OF TITRATION

(1) Direct titration.

IN the simple direct titration, the sample solution is adjusted to the required conditions by adding buffer, an auxiliary complex-forming substance if necessary, and an indicator. The EDTA is added until the colour change indicates the endpoint. The endpoint in direct titrations may also be detected by instrumental methods.

It should be noted that a direct titration may not always be applicable for the following reasons:

(*a*) It may not be possible to keep the metal ion in solution, because of too high a pH or the presence of a precipitating reagent.

(*b*) There may be no indicator available which gives a suitable colour reaction with the metal and an instrumental endpoint detection may not be applicable.

(*c*) The rate of the formation of the EDTA complex of the metal to be titrated may be too slow.

(*d*) The metal ion may not form a sufficiently stable complex (or none at all) to enable the titration to be made.

In these circumstances one of the following methods may be suitable.

(2) Back-titration.

A back-titration may help to overcome the first three difficulties mentioned above. A measured amount of EDTA is added in excess of that necessary to react with the metal to be titrated. The titration conditions are then adjusted, an indicator is added and the excess

59

of EDTA is back-titrated with a suitable metal salt solution until the indicator changes from its "free" colour to the "metallized" colour. (Alternatively an instrumental endpoint detection may be applied.)

It may be noted that the colour change in the back-titration does not indicate the "true" endpoint because a slight excess of metal ion solution must be added to provide sufficient metal ion to react with the indicator. When the amount of metal to be determined is large that drop or part of a drop of back-titrant is negligible. When, however, only a small amount of metal is titrated this error may become significant. The true endpoint is attained if the titration is finished by adding just enough EDTA to produce the colour of the free indicator. This amount of EDTA, of course, has to be taken into account in the calculation.

A back-titration procedure sometimes offers advantages even when a direct titration is applicable. The precision of the determination can be increased by using what we may call a "pendulum endpoint". Two burettes are used, one for the EDTA solution, the other for the back-titrant. The EDTA is added from the first burette in excess and the back-titration is done with the metal ion solution from the second burette until the colour of the metal-indicator complex appears. Then with a few drops of EDTA the colour of the free indicator is restored. The readings on both burettes are recorded. Now some more EDTA is added, back-titrated, and the final endpoint adjusted with EDTA. Again the readings on both burettes are recorded. This process is repeated once or twice. The average of the readings on each burette is taken as the basis of calculation.

This type of repeated endpoint decreases the drop error of the titration considerably. It is of special advantage if a titration is being done in which it is difficult to locate the endpoint sharply.

A further advantage of the method is that an overshooting of the endpoint is impossible. Back-titration may be helpful to salvage an over-titration if a direct titration has previously been applied.

(3) Titration involving a replacement reaction.

OF the four difficulties mentioned above, the first three have been shown to be eliminated by back-titration. A replacement titration can also be helpful in overcoming these three difficulties, and sometimes also the fourth. The replacement reaction is allowed to proceed and then the replaced ion is titrated directly. The reaction may be written as follows:

$$M + NY \rightleftarrows MY + N \qquad (10.1)$$

M denotes the metal to be determined which owing to one or more of the four points mentioned above cannot be titrated directly. N is a metal which can be titrated under the given conditions.

For solving a problem according to cases (a) to (d) a complex of metal N is added in at least an equivalent amount (an excess is better), and after the reaction has taken place the amount of N released (equivalent to the amount of M) is titrated.

The complex NY is usually an EDTA complex but it need not necessarily be so. The major consideration is that an equivalent amount of a metal is released, which can be titrated with EDTA (see the titration of silver in experiment 16.4, page 95).

It is important to note that when dealing with only the second difficulty an excess of replacement complex need not be added; an amount sufficient to replace enough metal N to give an endpoint is adequate. Hence we may differentiate between a total and a partial replacement titration.

A partial replacement titration may also be employed to improve an endpoint which would otherwise be rather poor with the metal M alone. Thus, magnesium- or zinc-EDTA complex may be added to improve the colour change for a lead titration using Erio T (see experiment 14.3, page 80). Addition of magnesium-EDTA complex is more or less essential when calcium is titrated using Erio T as indicator. In the absence of magnesium the endpoint is so poor that a correct result is difficult to obtain (experiment 14.5, page 81).

When a suitable replacement complex has to be selected the ratio of the stability constants of that complex and the titration complex must be taken into consideration. The indicator also plays an important rôle and in the titration all of the precautions necessary for the successful titration of the replaced metal N have to be observed. If, therefore, the lead titration is improved by addition of magnesium-EDTA complex, the slow endpoint of magnesium must be expected and warming of the solution may be advisable. This is not necessary if zinc-EDTA complex is added as the replacement complex; with the latter present, of course, cyanide ion cannot be used as masking reagent, because it would combine with the zinc.

Note that the relation between the stability of the indicator complex and the two metal-EDTA complexes is rather complicated. Generally, to promote the replacement reaction it would be expected that the stability constant of MY must be higher than that of NY, but the stability constant of the indicator complex alters the conditions considerably. If M does not form a complex with the indicator the equilibrium may be written

$$M + NY + I \rightleftarrows MY + NI \qquad (10.2)$$

where I denotes the indicator. It can be deduced that the equilibrium will be shifted the more to the right, the more stable the complex NI. If the stability of NI is sufficiently high, MY may be an even weaker complex than NY, yet the reaction will proceed to a satisfactory extent. For example in ammoniacal solution copper is displaced by calcium from its EDTA complex if PAN is present despite the fact that the stability of CuY is much higher than that of CaY.

(4) Indirect methods.

Sometimes none of the procedures mentioned above is applicable, yet an EDTA titration is still possible when special conditions are used.

Any quantitative precipitation reaction may be used provided that the compound formed contains the ion to be determined in a stoicheiometric ratio with a cation which can be titrated with EDTA. The amount of the first ion can then be calculated. For example, sodium can be precipitated as sodium zinc uranyl acetate and the zinc content of the isolated compound titrated. Sodium can be calculated since the ratio of $Zn : Na = 1 : 1$. Similarly potassium can be determined via a cobalt titration after precipitating as potassium cobaltinitrite.

An indirect method is also applicable to the determination of anions. Phosphate ion can be precipitated as magnesium ammonium phosphate and the magnesium is titrated after dissolving the precipitate (see experiment 17.1, page 97). Sulphate can be determined via titration of the barium present after precipitation of barium sulphate.

Halides may be determined via EDTA titration of silver (see experiment 17.2, page 99). Indirect methods have been applied to the determination of organic compounds. Acetylene can be absorbed from a gas stream in a copper salt solution; then the copper content of the dissolved precipitate can be titrated. Many organic bases can be precipitated with cadmium thiocyanate or BiI_4^- and the metal content of the precipitate is titrated with EDTA.

It may be worthwhile to note that it is not always necessary to titrate the solution of the precipitate. Alternatively a known amount of precipitating reagent may be added to the sample solution and the excess back-titrated in the filtrate.

Besides precipitation reactions a complexing reaction may also be helpful. For example, cyanide may be determined by adding the test solution to a measured volume of a nickel solution of known concentration. An amount of nickel equivalent to that of the cyanide ion is complexed and the excess nickel is back-titrated with EDTA.

Although quite an appreciable number of compounds can now be determined by EDTA titrations based on the principles mentioned above, the possibilities are not exhausted by far and further developments can be expected.

CHAPTER 11

STANDARD SOLUTIONS OF EDTA

ANALYTICALLY pure products of the free acid and of the salt $Na_2H_2Y \cdot 2H_2O$ are commercially available; both have been recommended as primary standards. The disodium salt usually contains up to about 0·3 per cent adsorbed moisture. If this is taken into consideration, for general purposes a sufficiently accurate solution may be obtained by weighing an appropriate amount, dissolving it and diluting to definite volume. The molecular weight of the disodium dihydrate salt is 372·2.

By drying under proper conditions a product can be obtained which corresponds fully to the above formula. The drying should be done at 50 per cent humidity (25° C) and 80° C over a period of 2–3 days. Higher temperatures must be avoided, otherwise some water of crystallization will be lost.

By drying at 150° C to constant weight the anhydrous salt is obtained, but is less suitable as primary standard because it tends to regain water of crystallization.

Investigations by Duval have shown via the thermogravimetric curves that the free acid is a considerably better primary standard. It contains no water of crystallization and is not hygroscopic. It can be dried without danger of decomposition at temperatures up to 150° C and even more. The molecular weight is 292·1.

(1) Preparation of a 0·100 M EDTA solution using the disodium salt.

Dissolve 37·22 g of the stoicheiometrically dried product in 500–800 ml of water in a 1 l. volumetric flask and after solution fill up to the mark. Use redistilled or deionized water (see "water", page 74).

If an analytical grade commercial product is used without special drying, weigh 37·29 g and proceed as described above. The titre will be within an accuracy of ±0·1−0·2 per cent which may be suitable for general purposes.

(2) Preparation of a 0·100 M EDTA solution using the acid.

Dry the analytically pure product for 2 hrs at about 130–150°C. Cool in a desiccator. Weigh 29·210 g. transfer to a 600 ml beaker and add about 600 ml of redistilled or deionized water. Add while stirring analytical grade sodium hydroxide, pellet by pellet, until the powder has dissolved. Transfer quantitatively to a 1 l. volumetric flask and dilute to the mark with redistilled or deionized water after room temperature has been reached.

Remark: Do not use sodium hydroxide solution from a glass bottle under any circumstances. Such solutions probably contain alkaline earths dissolved from the glass. A 50 per cent reagent grade sodium hydroxide solution may be used if stored in plastic bottles.

A convenient method of excluding cationic contamination of the solution is to dissolve the EDTA by bubbling ammonia gas from a cylinder into the slurry of the acid with water. Pass the gas stream through a washing bottle containing concentrated ammonia solution and some EDTA.

(3) More dilute EDTA standard solutions.

More dilute standard solutions can be obtained either by appropriate dilution of the 0·100 M stock solution, or by direct weighing of a suitable amount of disodium salt or free acid, and applying the above procedures.

(4) Storage of EDTA standard solutions.

Glass yields cations and anions to the EDTA solution, hence glass containers are unsuitable for storage (see experiment 7.3, page 40). A considerable decrease in the titre occurs if dilute EDTA solutions are stored in this way. For storage, only borosilicate glass containers should be used and preferably these should have been in use for a long time. To prevent such sources of error it is advisable (especially for micro work or for other procedures involving dilute solutions) to treat the container with a strongly alkaline EDTA solution (about 2 per cent) for several hours on a water bath before use. By this treatment "loose" metal ions are removed from the glass surface and the container may be safely used after thorough rinsing with redistilled or deionized water.

However, the best way is always to avoid glassware and to use polyethylene bottles.

The EDTA solutions (especially the more dilute), should be transferred immediately after their preparation from the volumetric glass flask into the polyethylene (or prepared glass) container.

(5) Stability of EDTA solution.

When the above mentioned precautions are strictly observed, the titre will be constant indefinitely. No change can be observed over a period of months even with $0 \cdot 001$ M EDTA solutions.

(6) Standardization of EDTA solutions.

Though both the disodium salt and the free EDTA can be used as primary standards, it may be necessary for various reasons to standardize the solution: e.g. only an impure product may be available; some impurities may have been introduced; a re-standardization may be found necessary; or it may be warranted because such extreme accuracy is required.

When impurities are present and high accuracy is desired, the standardization should be done under the same conditions as the actual titration. An example will illustrate the reason for this requirement. Suppose the impurities are calcium and zinc. If the standardization is performed in ammoniacal medium with a magnesium solution as reference, both zinc and calcium will react and consume their equivalent of EDTA. If the standardization is done as above but in the presence of potassium cyanide, zinc is masked and only calcium is active. If the standardization is done in acid medium with a bismuth solution as reference, neither calcium nor zinc react. Thus for the same solution three different titres are obtained according to the conditions under which the standardization is effected. For general purposes, however, sufficient accuracy will be achieved by standardizing against a zinc standard solution.

(7) 0·100 M zinc standard solution.

Method A: Place about 10 g of analytical grade zinc metal pellets in a 100 ml beaker and add 20 ml of hydrochloric acid (1 : 5) to dissolve any zinc oxide layer. Decant the acid and wash thoroughly by decantation with water. Then wash several times with ethanol and finally with ether. Dry the pellets. Weigh 6·537 g of the zinc metal and dissolve it in strong hydrochloric acid keeping the excess of acid as small as possible. To increase the rate of solution, boil and place a piece of platinum wire (about 3 cm long) into the beaker. After the zinc has dissolved, cool to room temperature and transfer the solution quantitatively to a 1 l. volumetric flask. Remove the platinum wire, if any has been added, during this operation. Dilute to the mark with redistilled or deionized water.

Method B: Ignite reagent grade zinc oxide for 20 min at 900°–1000° C and cool in a desiccator. Weigh exactly 8·137 g of the material and dissolve it in the minimum amount of hydrochloric acid necessary for complete reaction. Cool to room temperature, transfer to a 1 l. volumetric flask and dilute to the mark with redistilled or deionized water.

More dilute solutions may be prepared either by weighing smaller amounts of zinc metal or zinc oxide and following the above procedures, or by appropriately diluting the 0·100 M stock solution.

(8) Standardization procedure.

Place 20 or 25 ml portions (exactly measured with calibrated pipettes) of the standard zinc solution in a 250 ml conical flask. Add concentrated ammonia solution dropwise until the precipitate which first forms redissolves. Add 3 ml more of the ammonia. Add Erio T indicator powder and titrate with EDTA until the solution colour changes from red just to clear blue. Run at least a duplicate.

Calculation:

$$M_{EDTA} = \frac{A \times M_{Zn}}{B}$$

where M denotes the molarities of the solution named by the suffix, A is the millilitres of zinc solution taken, and B is the millilitres of EDTA required. Take the average of two, or more titrations.

Bibliography

(1) Purification and properties of disodium salt of EDTA as primary standard.
W. J. Blaedel and H. T. Knight, *Analyt. Chem.*, **26**, 741 (1954).

(2) Some reference standards for EDTA solutions.
P. F. Lott and K. L. Cheng, *Chemist-Analyst*, **47**, 8 (1958).

(3) The constancy of the titre of very dilute EDTA solutions.
H. Flaschka and F. Sadek, *Z. anal. Chem.* **156**, 23 (1957) (in German).

CHAPTER 12

REAGENTS AND SOLUTIONS

ALL reagents should be analytical grade. Only redistilled or deionized water should be used (see chapter 13, page 74) and the necessary precautions should be observed for storing the solutions (especially those which are alkaline).

(1) Metal ion solutions.

It is recommended that $0 \cdot 1$ M stock solutions be prepared; and $0 \cdot 01$ M solutions, which are used in the exercises, should be prepared by appropriate dilution of the stock solutions. The salts mentioned below are chosen because they should be readily available from the store-room and because they are of sufficient purity to provide the correct titre without any undue error. Of course, any other suitable compound, or the metal itself, may be used. The following list is arranged alphabetically and provides for 100 ml amounts of the $0 \cdot 1$ M solutions.

Aluminium. Dissolve $3 \cdot 75$ g $Al(NO_3)_3 \cdot 9H_2O$ in water containing 1 ml of concentrated HNO_3 and dilute to 100 ml with water.

Bismuth. Dissolve $4 \cdot 85$ g $Bi(NO_3)_3 \cdot 5H_2O$ in water containing 3 ml of concentrated HNO_3 and dilute to 100 ml with water.

Calcium. Dissolve $1 \cdot 00$ g $CaCO_3$ in the minimum amount of hydrochloric acid, boil off the carbon dioxide and dilute to 100 ml after having cooled to room temperature.

Chromium. Dissolve $4 \cdot 00$ g $Cr(NO_3)_3 \cdot 9H_2O$ in water containing 3 drops of concentrated HNO_3 and dilute to 100 ml.

Cobalt. Dissolve $2 \cdot 81$ g $CoSO_4 \cdot 7H_2O$ in water and dilute to 100 ml.

Copper. Dissolve $2 \cdot 50$ g $CuSO_4 \cdot 5H_2O$ in water and dilute to 100 ml.

Iron(III). Dissolve $4 \cdot 82$ g $FeNH_4(SO_4)_2 \cdot 12H_2O$ in water containing 5 drops of concentrated H_2SO_4 and dilute to 100 ml.

Lead. Dissolve $3 \cdot 31$ g $Pb(NO_3)_2$ in water and dilute to 100 ml.

Magnesium. Dissolve $0 \cdot 400$ g MgO (preferably freshly ignited) in the minimum amount of hydrochloric acid and dilute to 100 ml.

Manganese. Dissolve $1 \cdot 69$ g $MnSO_4 \cdot H_2O$ in water and dilute to 100 ml.

Mercury(II). Dissolve $3 \cdot 43$ g $Hg(NO_3)_2 \cdot H_2O$ in water and dilute to 100 ml.

Nickel. Dissolve $2 \cdot 63$ g $NiSO_4 \cdot 6H_2O$ in water and dilute to 100 ml.

Silver. Dissolve $1 \cdot 70$ g $AgNO_3$ in water containing 1 drop concentrated HNO_3 and dilute to 100 ml.

Zinc. See standard solution (page 67).

(2) Anion solutions (0·1 M).

Chloride. Dissolve $0 \cdot 585$ g NaCl in water and dilute to 100 ml.

Bromide. Dissolve $1 \cdot 19$ g KBr in water and dilute to 100 ml.

Iodide. Dissolve $1 \cdot 66$ g KI in water and dilute to 100 ml.

Phosphate. Dissolve $1 \cdot 42$ g Na_2HPO_4 in water and dilute to 100 ml.

(3) Indicators.

PAN, 0·05 per cent. Dissolve 50 mg of indicator in 100 ml of methanol or ethanol. (Stable.)

Pyrocatechol Violet, 0·1 per cent. Dissolve 100 mg of indicator in 100 ml of water. (Stable for about 2 months.)

Xylenol Orange, 0·1 per cent. Dissolve 100 mg of indicator in 100 ml water. The solution is stable.

Erio T indicator powder. Grind 100 mg of indicator with 10 g of NaCl to a very fine powder and store in a well-stoppered bottle. (Stable.)

Murexide indicator powder. Grind 500 mg of indicator with 10 g of NaCl to a very fine powder and store in a well-stoppered bottle. (Stable.)·

Benzidine, 0·1 per cent. Dissolve 100 mg of substance in 10 ml of glacial acetic acid.

Ferri-ferrocyanide mixture.

(a) Dissolve 1 g of potassium ferricyanide in 100 ml of water. The solution should be prepared freshly at least every week.

(b) Dissolve 1 g of potassium ferrocyanide in 100 ml of water. The solution is stable for several months.

Mix 10 ml (a) and 10 ml (b) and 80 ml water. The mixture must be prepared freshly every day.

Methyl red, 0·1 per cent. Dissolve 100 mg indicator in 100 ml of ethanol. (Stable.)

Phenolphthalein, 0·1 per cent. Dissolve 100 mg of substance in 100 ml of 80 per cent ethanol. (Stable.)

(4) Metal-EDTA complex solutions.

Mg-EDTA. Titrate two 20·00 ml portions of the 0·1 M magnesium solution with 0·100 M EDTA standard solution according to experiment 14.1, page 79). Take the average. Mix 20·00 ml of magnesium solution with exactly the amount of EDTA found in the titration. Shake well and store preferably in a plastic bottle. Transfer smaller amounts to a dropping bottle as needed.

Cu-EDTA. Titrate two 20·00 ml portions of the 0·01 M copper solution with 0·0100 M EDTA standard solution according to experiment 14.6, page 82. Take the average. Mix 20·00 ml of copper solution with exactly the amount of EDTA found in the titration. Shake well and store preferably in a plastic bottle: Transfer smaller amounts to a dropping bottle as needed.

Hg-EDTA. Titrate two 20·00 ml portions of the 0·01 M mercuric

solution with the 0·0100 M EDTA standard solution according to
experiment 16.2, page 93. Take the average. Mix 20·00 ml of the
mercuric solution with exactly the amount of EDTA solution required
in the titration. Add 5 drops of 1 N sodium hydroxide solution,
shake well and store preferably in a plastic bottle. Transfer smaller
amounts to a dropping bottle as needed.

(5) Preparation of potassium tetracyanonickelate.

Dissolve 10 g of $NiSO_4 \cdot 6H_2O$ in 10 ml water (stir well) and add
10 g of KCN. A honey-yellow liquid and a white precipitate (K_2SO_4)
are formed. Add 40 ml of ethanol, with stirring cool to room
temperature and filter through a Buchner funnel. Discard the
residue. To the filtrate add 200 ml of ethanol to precipitate the
tetracyanide, and filter through a Buchner funnel. Wash twice with
5 ml portions of ethanol. Spread the yellow crystals on paper,
cover to protect from dust and allow to stand for about two days
open to air. After that time any excess of potassium cyanide is
transformed to carbonate. The salt still contains some potassium
sulphate, but it does not interfere with the titrations. Grind the
salt if necessary and store in a bottle. The compound is stable.

(6) Buffer solutions.

It is especially important to observe all precautions mentioned
in chapter 13 concerning water, storage and purity of reagents when
the buffer solutions are prepared.

Buffer pH 10. Dissolve 70 g of NH_4Cl in 570 ml of ammonia
(s. g. 0·90) and dilute with redistilled water to 1 l. Transfer to a
plastic container or pretreated glass bottle.

Buffer pH 5. Dissolve 27·3 g of $NaC_2H_3O_2 \cdot 3H_2O$ in water containing 60 ml of 1 N HCl and dilute with redistilled water to 1 l.

(7) Miscellaneous reagents and solutions.

Sodium tartrate, 1 M. Dissolve 23 g of $Na_2C_4H_4O_6 \cdot 2H_2O$ in water
and dilute to 100 ml.

Potassium cyanide, 5 per cent.

Formaldehyde, 3 per cent.

Hydrogen peroxide, 3 per cent. and concentrated.

Ammonium acetate, 20 per cent.

Tartaric acid.

Ascorbic acid.

Metallic mercury.

0·1 N hydrochloric acid

1 N hydrochloric acid.

1:2 nitric acid.

1 M acetic acid.

0·1 N sodium hydroxide.

2 N sodium hydroxide.

Dilute acids and bases, bench reagent concentrations.

CHAPTER 13

HINTS FOR PRACTICAL WORK

ANY special precautions or particular measures to be observed are described under "remarks" at the appropriate place in the booklet. Despite this it is highly desirable to summarize some practical and important hints, since long experience has shown that neglect of certain points can cause serious trouble and lead to erroneous results.

(1) Water.

Many failures in the application of EDTA titrations are due to the impurities in the "distilled water", which sometimes actually does not deserve that term. Sometimes even more than trace amounts of calcium and/or magnesium can be found and these are naturally a source of error if such water is used for the preparation of a standard EDTA solution or of other reagent solutions. The situation is especially serious when titrations are done in an alkaline medium, because then alkaline earths complex with EDTA and are therefore titrated simultaneously.

Another impurity often found is copper, which originates from the distillation apparatus. The amount present may be so small that the result is in no way affected even if the trace is titrated. Many indicators, however, are seriously blocked by copper. Hence even this extremely small amount of copper can influence the colour change of the indicator to such a degree that a poor endpoint (or even no endpoint at all) is obtained. Accordingly only the purest redistilled or deionized water should be used. The following test is suitable to check the quality of the water.

74

(2) Purity test for water.

To about 50 ml of water, add 1 ml of buffer (pH 10) and an amount of Erio T indicator powder sufficient to cause just a faint colour. The colour of the solution should be blue. If the colour is violet or red, impurities are present. To ensure that the impurities do not originate from the buffer solution, add an EDTA solution dropwise (made by diluting 1 drop of 0·1 M EDTA with 10 ml of water). After the red colour has disappeared add 50 ml more of the water to be tested. If the red colour returns, the impurities are entering from the water. Add again EDTA dropwise until the solution is blue. Add 5 ml of buffer pH 10. If the colour turns red, the buffer also contains impurities. The number of drops of the very dilute EDTA solution needed to cause the colour change from red to blue is a rough measure of the degree of impurity. If the amount of impurity is very small, it may be tolerated.

Should the reddish tint not disappear after a considerable amount of EDTA has been added, add a crystal of potassium cyanide. If the solution turns blue, the impurity is most probably copper which is a more serious source of trouble.

To avoid any troubles due to impure water, it is best to purify the water by deionization. This is easily done by passing the impure distilled water through a strongly acidic cation exchange column (i.e. sulphonated type) in its hydrogen form. A column 2 cm in diameter and 15 cm long may be used to purify 500 or more litres of water before regeneration is necessary.

(3) pH control.

Metal indicators used in the EDTA titrations almost always show acid-base indicator properties or at least the colour of the metal-indicator complex is pH-dependent. Furthermore, metal-EDTA and metal-indicator complexes become weaker with increasing acidity. Therefore it is highly important that the proper pH value be attained. During the titration hydrogen ions are released (equation 3.2, page 21) and a fall in pH may result if the buffering is not adequate. This is especially important when titrations are done in a strongly acidic medium where buffers of sufficient capacity do not exist. Therefore in such titrations control and readjustment of pH is recommended, especially near the endpoint.

(4) Neutralization of the sample.

Many metal ion or reagent solutions used during the course of the titrations are acidic. It is not enough to add buffer to adjust them to the desired pH range. The acidity may be so high that the amount of buffer given in the description of the procedure is insufficient to provide the required pH. The amount of buffer required to give the correct pH can be so high that interference occurs because of the excessive salt concentration. Therefore neutralization is necessary. However, do not employ aqueous ammonia for this purpose! Always use sodium hydroxide or another strong base, unless it is otherwise stated for special reasons! Suppose a titration should be done at pH 10. The pH for the titration is adjusted by a buffer containing ammonia and ammonium ion in a certain ratio. If the neutralization is done with ammonia, the concentration of ammonium ion is increased and the pH obtained after addition of buffer will be lower than desired.

(5) Indicators.

Many indicators are not stable in solution and decompose more or less rapidly during storage; the solution should then be freshly prepared daily or weekly as may be necessary. Gradual decomposition of an indicator solution, especially if slow, will lead to a gradual decrease in the sharpness of the endpoint which may not be noticed from one day to the next.

The best way to overcome this indicator problem is to use the indicator in "solid dilution" form. Grind the indicator with an inert substance, such as reagent grade sodium chloride, potassium sulphate or sucrose etc. With a little experience it is an easy matter to estimate the appropriate amount of the powder which must be added to a certain volume of the sample solution to obtain the correct colour. It may be helpful to make a scoop of appropriate size from an aluminium sheet and to attach it to the stopper or cover of the container for the indicator mixture.

It is worthwhile to note that the degree of purity of commercially available indicators can differ considerably. Accordingly the amount of indicator recommended in any procedure for preparing a mixture or solution should be assumed to be only a rough figure.

This should always be considered when a screened indicator is prepared. It may be necessary to establish the proper ratio of the components experimentally for each new batch.

Some indicators are blocked by heavy metals, and traces of the latter must be excluded by addition of an appropriate masking reagent. It may be found convenient to avoid difficulties in any titration involving Erio T and any similar indicator by adding a crystal of potassium cyanide and of ascorbic acid. Cyanide, of course, is not permissible if a metal is to be titrated which itself forms cyano complexes.

Some indicators decompose quickly in strongly alkaline solution especially when hot. This is largely due to oxidation by air, a process which is often catalysed by heavy metal ions. Addition of ascorbic acid can often prevent this reaction. Nevertheless it should be taken as a basic rule to add the indicator to the solution to be titrated and then to start the titration without delay.

It sometimes happens that the described colour change of the indicator is altered by the colour of the solution. If a concentrated solution of a coloured ion is titrated or if a colour has been formed by prior addition of an acid-base indicator this should be taken into account. Any acid-base indicator added to neutralize the sample should be carefully selected so that the remaining colour will not interfere with the endpoint of the EDTA titration. The concentration of such an indicator must be kept as low as possible.

(6) Reagents.

An impurity in a reagent which may not influence the course of a particular classical procedure for a certain metal may cause considerable trouble when the same metal is titrated with EDTA. In ammoniacal medium this is especially so for alkaline earth impurities (see the section on "water", page 74) which are titrated simultaneously. The result for a metal with a high equivalent weight, such as lead, may then be seriously affected. Hence it is important to judge the purity requirements with that fact in mind. Metal ions are often introduced from the glass of the container, especially when strongly alkaline solutions such as sodium hydroxide, ammonia, buffer 10 solution etc., are stored in unsuitable containers. Plastic containers should be used for solutions of this kind.

Such impurities may not be critical in the course of the general experiments as described in this book, but they are certainly a definite source of error in micro work or in analyses where higher accuracy is demanded.

The points mentioned in this chapter may seem commonplace, but their neglect is the reason for the failure of an EDTA titration in nearly seven cases out of ten.

CHAPTER 14

EXAMPLES OF DIRECT TITRATIONS

For all metals titrated in the following experiments, there is a large number of methods known, differing in the technique applied and/or indicator used. The procedures selected in this chapter and those following are by no means claimed to be the best methods available at the present time. The selection has been made from the point of view of using as small a stock of reagents and indicators as possible, and to cover as many types of titrations as seemed feasible in an introductory text.

Experiment 14.1: Titration of magnesium. (Erio T.)

Theory: The titration of magnesium presents no difficulties except that the rate of reaction between the magnesium-Erio T complex and EDTA is somewhat low at room temperature. Either the titration must be done slowly or at an elevated temperature to overcome any errors due to the slow reaction. Interferences caused by traces of heavy metals may be excluded by addition of potassium cyanide according to the procedure outlined in chapter 9 (page 55).

Reagents: 0·01 M magnesium solution; 0·0100 M EDTA standard solution; buffer pH 10; dilute sodium hydroxide solution; Erio T indicator; powder methyl red, 0·1 per cent in ethanol.

Procedure: Place 10–40 ml (exactly measured) magnesium solution in a 250 ml conical flask. Dilute to about 50 ml, then add 5 ml of buffer and the indicator. Titrate slowly until the colour changes from red to blue. The correct endpoint is obtained when all traces of the red tint just disappear.

Alternatively proceed in exactly the same manner, but heat the solution to about 60° C and titrate at the usual rate.

Calculation: 1 ml 0·0100 M EDTA = 0·2731 mg Mg.

Remarks: If the magnesium solution is acid, neutralize with sodium hydroxide before adding the buffer. Methyl red may be used as acid-base indicator for the neutralization. This indicator may also be added as screening dye to obtain a somewhat sharper endpoint. The colour will then change from orange or dirty red to green or greenish blue, depending upon the amount of screening reagent added.

79

Experiment 14.2: Titration of zinc. (Erio T.)

Theory: Zinc can be titrated readily using Erio T as indicator at pH 10, or even at a somewhat lower pH. The solution must be ammoniacal so that the zinc-tetrammine complex is formed; this acts as an auxiliary complex to keep the zinc in solution at the prevailing pH.

Reagents: 0·01 M zinc solution; 0·0100 M EDTA standard solution; buffer pH 10; Erio T indicator powder.

Procedure: Place 10–30 ml (exactly measured) zinc solution in a 250-ml conical flask and dilute to about 50–100 ml. Add 5 ml of buffer and Erio T indicator and titrate until the colour changes from red to blue.

Calculation: 1 ml 0·0100 M EDTA = 0·6537 mg Zn.

Remarks: Note the extremely sharp endpoint in this titration. Even a small fraction of a drop of the EDTA solution can cause the disappearance of the last trace of red. Note further that the colour change is to a slightly greenish blue instead of the pure blue obtained in the magnesium titration (experiment 14.1, page 79).

Experiment 14.3: Titration of lead. (Erio T.)

Theory: Lead reacts with Erio T in ammoniacal medium. However at this pH the lead is precipitated as hydroxide. To avoid precipitation the addition of tartrate ion is necessary. The lead-tartrate complex is sufficiently stable to keep the lead in solution, but it is not sufficiently so to prevent its reacting with the indicator and with EDTA. Tartrate so used is called an "auxiliary complex-former". The colour intensity of the lead-Erio T complex is somewhat dependent upon the concentration of the tartrate and too large an excess of the auxiliary complex-former should be avoided. The colour of the indicator before the endpoint is a bluish violet. However the disappearance of the last reddish tint is very abrupt and takes place within the range of a drop or part of a drop of titrant. Compare the colour change at the endpoint of a magnesium titration (experiment 14.1, page 79), a zinc titration (experiment 14.2, above) and the lead titration. The colours before and after the endpoint are the most complementary in the case of magnesium. However the stability constant of the magnesium-Erio T complex and the ratio of this constant to that of the magnesium EDTA complex, are not sufficiently favourable to give a good endpoint. The colour change in the case of zinc is less complementary but the stability constants of the complexes involved and their ratio is much more favourable so that the endpoint is very brilliant. The complementary nature of the colours for lead is very poor, but the effect of the stability constants is favourable and the endpoint is, therefore, superior to that of magnesium. If a better complementary effect is desired the addition of magnesium- or zinc-EDTA complex can be recommended.

Reagents: 0·01 M lead solution; 0·0100 M EDTA standard solution; buffer pH 10; Erio T indicator powder; tartaric acid.

Procedure: Place. 10–30 ml (exactly measured) of 0·01 M lead solution in a 250 ml conical flask and add a spatula-end of tartaric acid. Add 5 ml of buffer pH 10 and dilute to about 50–100 ml. If a turbidity occurs add more tartaric acid. Add Erio T and titrate until the colour changes from violet just to clear blue.

Calculation: 1 ml 0·01 M EDTA = 2·0719 mg Pb.

Experiment 14.4: Titration of manganese(II). (Erio T.)

Theory: The direct titration of manganese in ammoniacal solution presents no difficulty provided that atmospheric oxygen is excluded or a reducing reagent such as ascorbic acid or hydroxylamine hydrochloride is added. In absence of a reducing agent, manganese(II) is oxidized by atmospheric oxygen to higher oxidation states. A brown precipitate may form, which reacts only very slowly with EDTA or reacts not at all. The main difficulty, however, is that manganese in its higher state of oxidation forms a very stable complex with the indicator. Thus the indicator is blocked and, moreover, it seems to decompose rapidly by catalyzed oxidation. For a detailed description and for experiments on this behaviour see experiment 7.6 (page 42).

Reagents: 0·01 M manganese(II) solution; 0·0100 M EDTA standard solution; buffer pH 10; Erio T indicator powder; ascorbic acid or hydroxylamine hydrochloride.

Procedure: Place 10–30 ml (exactly measured) of manganese solution in a 250 ml conical flask. Add a spatula-end of ascorbic acid, 5 ml of buffer pH 10 and dilute to about 100 ml. Add indicator and titrate until the colour changes from red to blue.

Calculation: 1 ml 0·0100 M EDTA = 0·5494 mg Mn.

Experiment 14.5: Titration of calcium. (Murexide.)

Theory: The titration of calcium in strong alkaline medium using murexide as indicator is a simple process. However the endpoint is not sharp. The colour change is insufficiently complementary (salmon red to violet) and the (apparent) stability constant of the calcium-murexide complex at pH 12 is only 10^5. This is rather low and actually very near to the permissible limit. Therefore many attempts have been made to improve the sharpness of the endpoint. Screening with a proper amount of a green, non-chelating dye, such as Naphthol Green B (CI 5) is helpful. The colour then changes from dirty red through olive to clear blue. Many procedures have been reported in which a photometric endpoint is applied as another means to overcome this difficulty (see experiment 21.3, page 132). This procedure is especially suitable in microtitrations. Other indicators are replacing murexide in the EDTA titration of calcium. A sharp endpoint is obtained with Calcon (CI 202), a dye with a structure similar to that of Erio T.

At pH 12 magnesium is precipitated as $Mg(OH)_2$ and does not interfere with the titration of calcium if present in moderate amounts (Ca : Mg about 1 : 5). This is a very important fact, because in practice calcium and magnesium are usually present together and their separation is tedious. (For titration of calcium and magnesium in the same solution see experiment 18.4, page 105.)

Reagents: 0·01 M calcium solution; 0·0100 M EDTA standard solution; 2 N sodium hydroxide; murexide indicator powder.

Procedure: Place 10–40 ml (exactly measured) of the calcium solution in a 250 ml conical flask, dilute to about 50 ml with water and add 5 ml of sodium hydroxide solution. Add murexide indicator to produce a clearly visible red colour and titrate immediately with EDTA until the colour changes to deep violet.

Calculation: 1 ml 0·0100 M EDTA = 0·4008 mg Ca.

Experiment 14.6: Titration of copper(II). (Murexide.)

Theory: The titration of copper using murexide as indicator does not involve any difficulties if care is taken to avoid too high a concentration of ammonia and ammonium ion. The copper-murexide complex is partially decomposed by high ammonia concentration owing to the conversion of the copper to the tetrammine complex (see experiment 7.11, page 45).

Reagents: 0·01 M copper solution 0·0100 M EDTA standard solution; buffer pH 10; murexide indicator.

Procedure: Place 10–20 ml (exactly measured) of copper solution in a conical flask. Add buffer pH 10 dropwise until the solution colour turns completely to blue and the precipitate first formed has redissolved. Dilute to 50–100 ml with water. If the solution becomes slightly milky add more buffer 10 dropwise. Add murexide indicator and titrate with EDTA until the colour changes from yellow (green) to deep violet.

Calculation: 1 ml 0·01 M EDTA = 0·6354 mg Cu.

Remarks: The copper-murexide complex is pure yellow, but the colour at the starting point of the titration is greenish depending on the amount of copper present. The green is the mixture of yellow (indicator complex) and blue (copper-tetrammine complex). As the titration proceeds the tetrammine complex is transformed to the less intensely coloured EDTA complex and the yellow of the indicator complex becomes predominant.

If the copper solution is acid a preneutralization should be done using sodium hydroxide rather than ammonia or buffer pH 10 (see page 76).

Experiment 14.7: Titration of nickel. (Murexide.)

Reagents: 0·01 M nickel solution; 0·0100 M EDTA standard solution; buffer pH 10; murexide indicator powder.

Procedure: Place 10–20 ml (exactly measured) of nickel solution in a conical flask. Add 5 ml of buffer pH 10 and dilute to about 50–100 ml. Add murexide indicator and titrate until the colour changes from yellow to deep violet.

Calculation: 1 ml 0·0100 M EDTA = 0·5871 mg Ni.

Remarks: The endpoint is very sharp. A few drops before the endpoint the colour changes to an orange tint. The final change to permanent deep violet is easily seen within a drop or fraction of a drop of EDTA solution. The complexing of nickel is somewhat slow; therefore if the titration is done at room temperature one has to titrate slowly near the equivalence point. The titration can be done at the usual speed if the solution is slightly warmed (50°–60° C). In this case, however, it is advisable to add the indicator just before the titration is started. In warm solutions the indicator sometimes decomposes rapidly.

Experiment 14.8: Titration of bismuth. (Pyrocatechol Violet.)

Theory: Bismuth can be determined by a simple direct titration using Pyrocatechol Violet as indicator. The colour properties of the bismuth-Pyrocatechol Violet complex are of interest. The colour is a deep corn-flower blue at about pH 2–3 which is the appropriate pH for the titration. At higher pH values the colour changes and further hydrolysis of the bismuth salts occurs. At lower pH values the colour becomes increasingly violet. Hence the indicator complex can be used to adjust and control the pH; this is important because of the tendency of bismuth salts to hydrolyse. The test solution is always strongly acidic and has to be neutralized to the proper pH before the titration is started. During the neutralization the indicator complex may serve as an acid-base indicator.

The colour change at the endpoint of the EDTA titration is extremely sharp because the yellow colour of the free indicator is almost fully complementary to that of the bismuth complex. If the titration is done with very dilute solutions the colour of the solution turns red just before the endpoint, because of a change in the ratio bismuth : indicator in the complex. This affords a warning that the endpoint is near. Also when more concentrated solutions are used this warning occurs because the red colour in the neighbourhood of the added drop disappears only slowly during the shaking of the titration vessel.

Reagents: 0·01 M bismuth nitrate solution; 0·0100 M EDTA standard solution; Pyrocatechol Violet, 0·1 per cent in water; dilute aqueous ammonia; universal indicator paper.

Procedure: Place 10–20 ml of bismuth nitrate solution (exactly measured) in a 250 ml conical flask, add 3–4 drops of indicator solution and dilute to about 100-150 ml. The solution should be clear blue. If not, add carefully dilute ammonia dropwise until the violet changes to blue. Be careful not to produce a permanent turbidity by local excess of alkali. Check that the pH is about 2 with indicator paper. Titrate until the colour changes to clear yellow.

Calculation: 1 ml 0·0100 M EDTA = 2·090 mg Bi.

Remarks: If the amount of bismuth is large, an appreciable amount of hydrogen ions is released during the titration (see equation 3.2, page 21). Therefore the pH should be checked several times during the titration either by indicator paper or by observing the colour of the bismuth-indicator complex. This is especially important in the vicinity of the endpoint. If the concentration of bismuth is high, it may be difficult to adjust the pH properly without producing a turbidity due to hydrolysis. Such turbidity will disappear during the titration but only very slowly and at the expense of considerable working time. In such an event, the solution should be diluted sufficiently or the titration is started in an incomplete neutralized medium (violet colour of the indicator complex) and the final adjustment made when the endpoint is imminent. That the endpoint is near can be recognized easily by the fact that the yellow or red colour in the region of the entering drops of titrant disappear sluggishly. Unfortunately no buffer of sufficient capacity exists for the pH range of the bismuth titration.

Since bismuth oxychloride hydrolyzes readily the presence of chloride may cause serious trouble when the pH is adjusted. If large amounts of chloride are present a back-titration procedure is preferable.

The acid test-solution is treated with an excess of EDTA, the pH is appropriately adjusted and then the excess of EDTA is back-titrated with a standard bismuth solution.

The determination of bismuth is highly selective and only a few metals, which form very stable EDTA complexes, interfere because they are titrated simultaneously. It is especially noteworthy that the determination of bismuth can be done in the presence of even large amounts of lead. Iron(III) is masked by addition of ascorbic acid (which reduces it to ferrous iron). Thorium can be titrated in exactly the same manner as bismuth. The colour change at the endpoint, however, is not so sharp.

Experiment 14.9: Titration of copper(II). (PAN.)

Theory: The high stability of the copper(II)-EDTA complex permits the titration of copper(II) even in acetic acid medium. This is important because under this condition alkaline earths, and, if present in small amounts, manganese do not interfere. The titration presents no difficulties except that the reaction between the copper-PAN complex and EDTA takes place very slowly at room temperature. This is most probably due to the insolubility of copper-PAN in aqueous solution leading to a colloidal form of the indicator complex. If the determination is done very slowly near the endpoint, serviceable results can be obtained but precision and accuracy are not very high. This difficulty is circumvented by titrating in boiling solution or preferably by adding an organic solvent. In a solution containing 50 per cent ethanol or acetone the colour change at the endpoint is rapid.

Reagents: 0·01 copper(II) solution; 0·0100 M EDTA standard solution; acetate buffer pH 5; PAN, 0·05 per cent in ethanol; ethanol or acetone.

Procedure: Place 10–20 ml (exactly measured) of the copper solution in a 250 ml conical flask and dilute to about 50 ml. Add 50 ml of ethanol (or acetone), 5 ml of buffer pH 5 and 3-5 drops of PAN indicator. Titrate until the deep red-violet changes to canary yellow.

Calculations: 1 ml 0·0100 M EDTA = 0·6354 mg Cu.

Experiment 14.10: Titration of iron(III). (Potassium thiocyanate.)

Theory: Iron(III) gives colour reactions with many complex-forming reagents, some of which can be used as indicators, e.g. thiocyanate, salicylic acid, sulphosalicylic acid, Tiron (sodium dihydroxybenzenedisulphonate) and others. The titration is best done at pH 2–3. At lower pH values some of these indicator complexes and the iron-EDTA complex are too highly dissociated. At higher pH iron(III) tends to hydrolyse.

Iron(III) reacts only slowly with the EDTA and therefore the titration must be done slowly or at elevated temperatures to avoid error. The temperature must not be raised above 40–50° C to avoid hydrolysis. The colour change at the endpoint may be affected somewhat by the concentration of iron because of the yellow colour of the iron(III)-EDTA complex. The solution at the endpoint is colourless only at very low concentrations of iron(III).

It should be remarked that hardly any indicator for iron(III) gives entirely satisfactory endpoints and detection by instrumental means or a back-titration procedure may give better results. However the direct titration has the advantage of speed and of relatively high selectivity.

Reagents: 0·01 M iron(III) solution; 0·0100 M EDTA standard solution; dilute aqueous ammonia; dilute hydrochloric acid; sodium acetate; potassium thiocyanate; universal indicator paper.

Procedure: Place 10–20 ml (exactly measured) of iron solution in a 250 ml beaker and add a spatula-end of sodium acetate and potassium thiocyanate. If the solution is strongly acidic it is nearly always colourless. Add ammonia dropwise until the solution becomes deep red. Now adjust the pH to 2–3 using ammonia or hydrochloric acid as necessary (use indicator paper). Warm to 40–50° C and titrate while stirring well until the red colour fades completely to colourless or slightly yellow.

Calculation: 1 ml 0·0100 M EDTA = 0·5585 mg Fe.

Remarks: According to equation 3.2 (page 21) during the titration hydrogen ions are released. The capacity of the buffer in the range being employed is very low. If large amounts of iron are present the pH may drop below the permissible limit. Therefore during the titration (and especially near the endpoint) control of pH is advisable and it should be readjusted if necessary.

CHAPTER 15

EXAMPLES OF BACK-TITRATIONS

Experiment 15.1: Titration of nickel. (PAN, back-titration with Cu.)

Theory: Nickel, like many other metals, forms a deeply coloured complex with PAN. The intensity of the colour is not as high as that of the corresponding copper complex, but, other things being equal, would be sufficient to provide a good endpoint. However, nickel reacts very slowly in this particular complex reaction and a direct titration is impossible because nickel almost completely blocks the indicator. Addition of alcohol or boiling or even both do not improve matters significantly as is the case with copper. A partial replacement titration may be applied as described in experiment 16.2, page 93, or a back-titration procedure incorporated with advantage.

Reagents: 0·01 M nickel solution; 0·0100 M EDTA standard solution; 0·01 M copper solution to be standardized; acetate buffer pH 5; PAN. 0 05 per cent in ethanol.

Procedure: Place 10–20 ml (exactly measured) of nickel solution in a 250 ml conical flask. Add EDTA solution in excess over the amount of nickel. Add 5 ml of pH 5 buffer and 3–5 drops of indicator. Dilute to about 100 ml and titrate the yellow solution with the copper solution until the colour just changes to violet. Add a few drops of EDTA to restore the colour just to yellow. Take the readings on both burettes. Add some more EDTA and titrate again with copper to violet and then with EDTA just to yellow. Take the readings of both burettes again. Repeat the endpoint adjustment once or twice more. Average the readings on the EDTA burette; let this amount be A ml. Average the readings on the copper burette and let this amount be B ml.

Standardize the copper solution by titrating two 20 ml portions following the procedure in experiment 14.9 (page 85). Take the average of the two titrations.

Calculation: From the data of the standardization procedure the molarity of the copper solution is calculated by

$$M_{Cu} = \frac{\text{ml EDTA} \times 0 \cdot 01}{\text{ml copper solution}}$$

$$(A \times 0 \cdot 01 - B \times M_{Cu}) \times 58 \cdot 71 = \text{mg Ni}$$

Remarks: For the advantages of the repeated or "pendulum" endpoint see chapter 10 (2). page 59. Copper as back-titrant has certain limitations. If solutions more concentrated than $0 \cdot 01$ M are used, the colour of the copper-EDTA complex is so deep that the endpoint is obscured. especially if the excess of EDTA added is large. In such circumstances it is advisable to run a preliminary titration with an aliquot of the sample, to estimate roughly how much of the nickel (or any other metal to be titrated) is present. Then in the final titration the excess of EDTA to be added can be controlled.

Boiling or addition of alcohol is not necessary (compare experiment 14.9, page 85). During the back-titration the complex formation between copper and PAN takes place almost instantaneously. Hence only a very small amount of copper has to be titrated with EDTA to reach the correct endpoint. For this purpose only one or two drops of EDTA solution are necessary, and the 10–15 sec between each addition does not require much time.

The method can be applied in exactly the same manner to the determination of cobalt, iron, lead, bismuth; and at pH 6 of zinc and cadmium. Some other metals may also be titrated. When aluminium is titrated the solution must be boiled for 2 min before starting the back-titration. (See experiment 15.2, below.)

Experiment 15.2: Titration of aluminium. (Ferri-ferrocyanide-benzidine.)

Theory: The redox potential, E, of the ferri-ferrocyanide system in water is given by the Nernst equation

$$E = E^\circ + 0 \cdot 0591 \times \log \frac{\text{(ferricyanide)}}{\text{(ferrocyanide)}} \tag{15.1}$$

where E° is a constant.

Over a wide pH range the potential is independent of the acidity of the solution, and at a pH of about 5, benzidine (i.e. *p*-diaminodiphenyl) is not oxidized by ferricyanide if a small concentration of ferrocyanide is present. If zinc ion is added to such a solution, the very slightly soluble zinc ferrocyanide is formed and the potential is increased, because the concentration of free ferrocyanide is decreased. At the higher potential benzidine is oxidized to a blue-coloured form. If EDTA is added to such a solution the zinc-EDTA complex is formed, which is sufficiently stable to remove the zinc from zinc ferrocyanide. The concentration of the free ferrocyanide is increased, the potential is decreased to the initial value and benzidine is reduced to the colourless form.

By this redox mechanism the endpoint in a zinc titration can be detected. However, it must be realized that the endpoint will be very slow because the reaction between the colloidal zinc ferrocyanide and EDTA will be time-consuming. On the other hand the reverse titration, namely, that of EDTA with a zinc solution, is accompanied by a rather rapid colour change at the equivalence point, because the formation of zinc ferrocyanide is a fast reaction. Therefore a back-titration procedure is appropriate for this type of endpoint. If an excess of EDTA is back-titrated with zinc solution using the ferri-ferrocyanide-benzidine endpoint, many metals can be determined including iron(III), aluminium, zinc, nickel, copper, lead, bismuth and some others.

The back-titration in this instance has some additional advantages. For example, if zinc should be titrated directly, traces of copper and iron(III) present in the solution will also form insoluble ferrocyanides but these react so very slowly with EDTA that the indicator system is practically blocked. In a back-titration, however, the interfering metals are complexed by EDTA and therefore interference is eliminated.

In the following procedure only the determination of aluminium is described because it behaves characteristically in EDTA titrations. The aluminium-EDTA complex forms only very slowly. Unless the EDTA is added in large excess, the titration will always give low results if done in the usual way. The reason is as follows: in order to avoid hydrolysis, the aluminium solution is always rather acid and must be neutralized after the addition of EDTA. Because of the slow rate of complexing during the neutralization there remains always some uncomplexed aluminium. Accompanying the addition of each drop of ammonia or sodium hydroxide, local excesses of alkali occur. This causes hydrolysis of the uncomplexed aluminium, and if the pH is locally raised sufficiently, aluminium may also be released from the EDTA complex which has already formed. A visible precipitation may not occur, but aluminium is transformed to hydroxo-compounds, which age quickly and do not later react readily with EDTA.

Special precautions are therefore necessary to ensure that all aluminium has been transformed into the EDTA complex before the back-titration is started. The considerations necessary to fulfil this condition include:

(a) Addition of a large excess of EDTA, so that its concentration will speed the complex formation and shift the equilibrium to the favourable side.

(b) Neutralizątion at first only to a pH of about 1–2 at which the slow reacting hydroxo-complexes or compounds are not formed; then the final pH is adjusted by addition of sufficient buffer, thus avoiding over-alkalification.

(c) A long standing period before starting the back-titration to provide sufficient time for complex formation.

(d) Heating the solution to increase the rate of complex formation. Boiling for 1–2 min will transform all aluminium into the EDTA complex.

However, the back-titration has to be done in cold solution, otherwise the increased solubility of zinc ferrocyanide would result in an insufficient increase in redox potential.

The endpoint with 3,3′-dimethylnaphthidine (instead of benzidine) is superior and the colour change from red to colourless is sharper. Benzidine, however, is more readily available and functions satisfactorily for general purposes.

It is surprising that the redox system functions with the smallest traces of ferrocyanide (0·005 per cent) present in reagent grade potassium ferricyanide. When benzidine is used, addition of a minute amount of ferrocyanide is advisable, and the sample solution must be free of sulphate ion because the indicator system is blocked by the formation of the insoluble benzidine sulphate.

Reagents: 0·01 M aluminium solution; 0·0100 M EDTA standard solution; 0·01 M zinc solution to be standardized; freshly prepared ferri-ferrocyanide solution (see page 67); benzidine solution, 1 per cent in glacial acetic acid; buffer pH 5; phenolphthalein, 0·1 per cent in ethanol; dilute sodium hydroxide solution.

Procedure: Place 10–30 ml (exactly measured) of aluminium solution in a 250 ml conical flask, and add EDTA in an amount in excess of the equivalent of aluminium taken. Add a few drops of phenolphthalein solution and then sodium hydroxide until a pink colour persists. Now add 10 ml of buffer pH 5, heat, and boil for 2 min. Cool to room temperature and dilute to about 100 ml. Add 1 ml of ferri-ferrocyanide solution and a few drops of the benzidine solution. Back-titrate slowly with zinc solution under vigorous shaking until a blue colour appears. Immediately titrate with a few drops of EDTA (waiting 15 sec after the addition of each drop) until the solution is colourless or slightly yellow (colour of ferricyanide). Standardize the zinc solution by the same procedure using zinc solution instead of the aluminium solution, and carry out two titrations with about 20 ml portions.

Calculations: The molarity of the zinc solution is calculated by

$$M_{Zn} = \frac{\text{ml EDTA} \times 0 \cdot 01}{\text{ml zinc solution}}$$

If the total amount of EDTA required is A ml and that of the zinc required is B ml, the calculation becomes:

$$(A \times 0 \cdot 01 - B \times M_{Zn}) \times 26 \cdot 98 = \text{mg Al.}$$

Remarks: Be sure that the solution is free from sulphate if benzidine is used. The back-titration should be started after the solution has cooled to room temperature, which may be hastened by cooling the outside of the conical flask under the tap. If the pH during the titration is too low the colour of the endpoint is not blue but intensely yellow.

If 3,3'-dimethylnaphthidine is available, use a 0·3 per cent solution in glacial acetic acid. The colour of the endpoint in the back titration is deep red.

Fe(III), Zn, Cd, Ni, Cu, Pb and Bi can be titrated in exactly the same way, except that the boiling is omitted.

Bibliography
(1) The use of the zinc ferro-ferricyanide redox system.
E. G. Brown and T. J. Hayes, *Analyt. Chim. Acta,* **9**, 6 (1953).
(2) The application of the indicator system according to Brown and Hayes.
H. Flaschka and W. Franschitz, *Z. anal. Chem.*, **144**, 421 (1955) (in German).
(3) The volumetric determination of aluminium in non-ferrous alloys.
G. W. C. Milner and J. L. Woodhead, *Analyst,* **79**, 363 (1954).
(4) Rapid determination of aluminium using a complexometric method.
I. Sajo, *Acta Chim. Hungaria,* **6**, 251 (1955) (in German).

Experiment 15.3: Titration of nickel. (Erio T; back-titration with Mg.)

Theory: Nickel forms a very stable complex with Erio T, which is in fact stronger than the corresponding EDTA complex. Nickel, however, is very slow in most of its complex formation reactions. If, therefore, Erio T is added to a solution containing nickel combined as its EDTA complex, a considerable time is needed for it to change over to the Erio T complex. Hence an excess of EDTA can be back-titrated with magnesium solution using Erio T as indicator (see experiments 7.7 and 7.8, page 43).

Reagents: 0·01 M nickel solution; 0·0100 M EDTA standard solution; 0·01 M magnesium solution to be standardized; buffer pH 10; Erio T indicator powder.

Procedure: Place 10–20 ml (exactly measured) of nickel solution in a 250 ml conical flask. Add EDTA solution in an amount which is in excess over the nickel. Add 5 ml of buffer pH 10 and dilute to 50–100 ml. Add Erio T and titrate with magnesium solution until the colour changes from blue just to red. Titrate with a few drops of EDTA until the colour just returns to blue.

Standardize the magnesium solution using a 20 ml portion following the procedure in experiment 14.1 (page 79). Repeat the titration and take the average.

Calculation: The molarity of the magnesium solution is calculated by

$$M_{Mg} = \frac{ml\ \text{EDTA} \times 0\cdot01}{ml\ Mg\ \text{solution}}$$

$$(A \times 0\cdot01 - B \times M_{Mg}) \times 58\cdot71 = mg\ Ni$$

where A denotes the total amount of ml EDTA and B is the amount in millilitres magnesium solution required in the titration of nickel.

Remarks: Do not add the indicator before EDTA and buffer have been added. Start the titration at once after the addition of the indicator. Titrate quickly to avoid blocking of the indicator. Once the indicator is blocked reject the sample.

CHAPTER 16

EXAMPLES OF REPLACEMENT TITRATIONS

Experiment 16.1: Titration of calcium. (Mg-EDTA, Erio T.)

Theory: Calcium gives only a very weak complex with Erio T and there-fore a simple direct titration is not possible using this indicator. If, however, magnesium is present calcium is complexed at first, and then magnesium; the reaction of the latter with Erio T furnishes the end point. This is very important for the titration of the sum Ca + Mg (see experiment 18.4, page 105). When no magnesium is present it may be added as magnesium EDTA complex so that calcium is titrated via a partial replacement titration. At least 5 per cent magnesium (calculated on the basis of calcium present) should be added to ensure a satis-factory endpoint.

Reagents: 0·01 M calcium solution; 0·0100 M EDTA standard solution; buffer pH 10; Erio T indicator powder; 0·05 M magnesium-EDTA solution (for preparation, see page 71).

Procedure: Place 10–30 ml (exactly measured) of calcium solution in a 250 ml conical flask. Add 5 ml of magnesium-EDTA solution, 5 ml of buffer pH 10, and dilute to about 50 ml. Heat to about 60° C, add Erio T indicator and titrate until the colour changes from red to clear blue.

Calculation: 1 ml 0·0100 M EDTA = 0·4008 mg Ca.

Remarks: Observe all precautions for a magnesium titration as described in experiment 14.1 (page 79).

Experiment 16.2: Titration of mercury(II). (Mg-EDTA, Erio T.)

Theory: Mercury forms amino complexes which are sufficiently stable to keep mercury from being precipitated at higher pH values. The stability of these auxiliary complexes, however, is less than that of the EDTA complex so that a partial replacement titration is possible using mag-

93

nesinm-EDTA complex for the replacement reaction.

Reagents: 0·01 M mercury solution; 0·0100 M EDTA standard solution; 0·05 M magnesium-EDTA solution (for preparation see page 71); buffer pH 10; dilute sodium hydroxide; Erio T indicator powder; methyl red, 0·1 per cent in ethanol.

Procedure: Place 10–30 ml (exactly measured) of mercury solution in a 250 ml conical flask. If the solution is strongly acidic add 2 drops methyl red indicator and neutralize with sodium hydroxide until the colour turns to yellow. Do not be alarmed if a precipitate or turbidity occurs. Now add buffer dropwise until the white precipitate formed initially is completely dissolved. Add 3 ml of buffer in excess and 5 ml 0·05 M Mg-EDTA solution. Then add indicator and titrate until the colour changes from red to blue.

Calculation: 1 ml 0·0100 M EDTA = 2·0059 mg Hg.

Remarks: Observe all precautions necessary in a magnesium titration (experiment 14.1, page 79). Alternatively the titration may be done at elevated temperatures. If the concentration of mercury is high it may happen that a slight turbidity persists. It will disappear during the course of the titration. If methyl red has been added the colour change may go to green (screened indicator).

Experiment 16.3: Titration of lead. (Cu-EDTA-PAN.)

Theory: As shown in experiment 14.3 (page 80), the titration of lead in ammoniacal solution is a simple operation. However because of the high equivalent weight of lead any calcium and magnesium impurities, which may often be present, cause high results for lead. Since alkaline earths do not complex with EDTA in acid medium, a titration under acid conditions enables this source of error to be avoided. A partial replacement titration which involves the copper-EDTA-PAN system. Lead can also be titrated directly, in slightly acidic medium using Xylenol Orange as indicator. See experiment 18.1.

Reagents: 0·01 M lead solution; 0·0100 M EDTA standard solution; acetate buffer pH 5; PAN, 0·05 per cent in ethanol; copper-EDTA solution 0·05 M (for preparation see page 71); ethanol or acetone.

Procedure: Place 10–30 ml (exactly measured) lead solution in a 250 ml conical flask. Add 5 ml of buffer pH 5 (after the sample solution has been neutralized if necessary), 5 drops of copper-EDTA solution, and 3–5 drops of indicator solution and dilute to about 50 ml. Add 50 ml of ethanol or acetone and titrate until the colour changes from red to yellow.

Calculation: 1 ml 0·0100 M EDTA = 2·0719 mg Pb.

Remarks: Observe all precautions for a copper titration as given in experiment 14.9 (page 85). Take care to add the indicator *after* the solution has been fully adjusted for the titration.

The procedure given for lead serves as an example of a general method. Many other metal ions can be titrated in the same manner including nickel, cobalt and at pH 6 zinc and cadmium. Aluminium can be titrated in strongly acetic acid medium in boiling solution.

Experiment 16.4: Titration of silver. ($Ni(CN)_4^{-2}$, murexide.)

Theory: It is not possible to titrate silver directly with EDTA because the Ag-EDTA complex is not sufficiently stable. It can, however, be determined after a replacement reaction. If a silver solution is added to an ammoniacal solution of potassium tetracyanonickelate solution, the following reaction takes place:

$$[Ni(CN)_4]^{-2} + 2\ Ag^+ \rightleftharpoons 2\ [Ag(CN)_2]^- + Ni^{+2} \qquad (16.1)$$

Silver has a higher affinity for the cyanide ion than nickel and thereby releases an equivalent amount of nickel, which can be titrated using murexide indicator. The above reaction takes place, even if a water-insoluble silver salt is introduced in the complex-containing solution. This fact allows the simple determination of silver after it has been separated from other metal ions by precipitation. It is the basis of an indirect determination of halide ions too (see experiment 17.2, page 99).

Reagents: 0·01 M silver solution; 0·0100 M EDTA standard solution; buffer pH 10; murexide indicator powder; potassium tetracyanonickelate (for preparation see page 72).

Procedure: Dissolve 0·2–0·3 g of potassium tetracyanonickelate in about 50 ml water in a 250 ml conical flask. Add 5 ml of buffer pH10 and murexide indicator. Place 10–30 ml (exactly measured) of silver solution in the flask and titrate with EDTA until the colour changes from yellow to violet.

Calculation: According to the above equation two silver ions are equivalent to one released nickel ion.

$$1 \text{ ml } 0{\cdot}0100 \text{ M EDTA} = 2{\cdot}1574 \text{ mg Ag.}$$

Remarks: Observe all precautions for a nickel titration according to experiment 14.7, page 83. The equivalent weight of silver is twice as much in this titration as in a classical halide titration. This somewhat unfavourable fact is balanced to a great extent by the extreme sharpness of the endpoint.

Bibliography

(1) The indirect determination of silver and halogens.
H. Flaschka and F. Huditz, *Z. anal. Chem.*, **137**, 104 (1952) (in German).

CHAPTER 17

EXAMPLES OF INDIRECT DETERMINATIONS

Experiment 17.1: Determination of phosphate.

Theory: Phosphate ion can be precipitated with magnesium from strongly ammoniacal solutions giving a salt of the composition $MgNH_4PO_4.6H_2O$. Because the molar ratio $Mg : PO_4^{-3}$ is exactly $1 : 1$ if the precipitation is made under proper conditions, a titration of the magnesium allows calculation of the phosphate present. If the precipitate is dissolved in acid and an excess of EDTA is added, the solution can be made alkaline and no precipitate is formed because the magnesium is sufficiently strongly complexed by the EDTA. The excess of EDTA can then be back-titrated with magnesium solution. If only very small amounts of precipitate are obtained, the acid solution of the salt may be made ammoniacal and directly titrated without occurrence of a precipitate. Magnesium ammonium phosphate forms supersaturated solutions, and precipitation may be delayed even if magnesium or phosphate is present in considerable excess. In the titration, however, there are only equivalent amounts present and this favours the non-occurrence of a reprecipitation after addition of ammonia buffer.

In the course of the back-titration, this also explains why the minute excess of magnesium solution does not form a precipitate; furthermore this magnesium combines with the indicator. It should be noted that precipitation of the phosphate can be made in the presence of EDTA and tartaric acid (as masking reagent) thus effecting a greater selectivity and freedom from interferences. Magnesium is not the only metal which forms insoluble phosphates; calcium and many of the heavy metals do so under the precipitation conditions. Therefore separations are necessary and make the classical analysis quite tedious. Magnesium forms an EDTA complex much lower in stability than all the interfering metals. Thus if a solution is treated with excess of EDTA all metals are complexed and no turbidity occurs when ammonia is added. The addition of "magnesia mixture" will at first complex the "free" EDTA. Then any further magnesium added will precipitate the phosphate. Iron, aluminium and some other trivalent metal ions may be replaced partly or

97

completely by magnesium from their EDTA complexes and be precipitated either as phosphates or hydroxides. This would cause difficulties
during the titration and give erroneous results. For complete masking
of these metals addition of tartrate or citrate is necessary. Lactate has
also been recommended and is claimed not to delay the precipitation
of the magnesium phosphate as the other reagents do to some extent.

Reagents: 0·01 M phosphoric acid or sodium phosphate. 0·0100 M EDTA
standard solution; 0·01 M magnesium solution to be standardized;
aqueous ammonia; magnesia mixture; dilute hydrochloric acid; Erio T
indicator powder; methyl red indicator, 0·1 per cent in ethanol; dilute
sodium hydroxide solution.

Procedure: Place 10–30 ml (exactly measured) of the phosphate solution
in a 400 ml beaker, add magnesia mixture (5 ml) and heat to boiling. Add
aqueous ammonia dropwise with stirring, until a crystalline precipitation
forms. Add 5 ml of ammonia in excess and allow to stand for about
2 hr. Filter through a sintered glass crucible and wash with 1 per cent
ammonia solution (buffer pH 10 diluted 1 : 20 with water is a suitable
wash solution). There is no need to remove the particles adhering to
the wall of the beaker. Remove the filtrate from the suction flask and
clean the flask. Mount the crucible again on the flask but do not connect
with the vacuum line. Place a few millilitres of dilute hydrochloric
acid in the crucible and stir with a glass rod to dissolve the precipitate.
When all the salt has dissolved apply suction and then rinse the crucible
quantitatively with water. Transfer the solution from the flask to the
beaker in which the precipitation was done. Wet the wall of the beaker
with the solution to ensure that all the adhering particles have dissolved.
Add EDTA in an amount sufficient to ensure an excess over the magnesium present. Add 1 drop of methyl red and neutralize with sodium
hydroxide solution until the colour turns to yellow. Dilute to 150 ml
with water, add 5 ml of buffer pH 10 and Erio T indicator. Titrate with
magnesium solution until the colour turns red. Titrate with EDTA
solution just to clear blue. Standardize the magnesium solution by
titrating two separate portions (about 20 ml) with EDTA applying the
procedure described in experiment 14.1 (page 79).

Calculation: Calculate the molarity of the magnesium solution, M_{Mg}, and
take the average of the two determinations

$$M_{Mg} = \frac{\text{ml EDTA} \times 0·0100}{\text{ml Mg solution}}$$

$$(\text{Total ml EDTA} \times 0·01 - \text{ml} \times M_{Mg}) \times 30·974 = \text{mg P}$$

Remarks: Observe all precautions for a magnesium titration according to experiment 14.1 (page 79).

If the phosphate solution contains other metal ions, such as calcium, iron, manganese, aluminium, copper, etc., sufficient EDTA (in the form of a more concentrated solution) and some tartaric acid are added to the acid solution before the precipitation is started. It is also advisable to add some potassium cyanide and a few crystals of ascorbic acid to the titration solution to prevent any interferences caused by heavy metals, traces of which may contaminate the precipitate.

If very small amounts of phosphate are being determined, the back-titration procedure may be unnecessary for the reasons mentioned in the theoretical part above. In such a case neutralize the acid solution of the precipitate, dilute to 150–200 ml with water, add buffer pH 10 and indicator and start the titration at once.

Experiment 17.2: Determination of chlorine, bromine or iodine.

Theory: The reaction between silver and the potassium tetracyano-nickelate (equation (16.1), page 95) also proceeds with insoluble silver salts such as the chloride, bromide and iodide. Warming is necessary to increase the rate of dissolution of the last compound which occurs as the exchange reaction proceeds. Based on this exchange reaction an indirect determination becomes possible for the halogens (other than fluoride) after their precipitation as the silver salt.

Reagents: 0·01 M solutions of potassium chloride, bromide or iodide; 0·0100 M EDTA standard solution; buffer pH 10; dilute nitric acid; 5 per cent nitrate solution; potassium tetracyanonickelate (for preparation see page 72); murexide powder indicator.

Procedure: Place 10–20 ml (exactly measured) of a halide solution in a 400 ml beaker, dilute to about 100 ml with water, add 5 drops of nitric acid and heat to boiling. Precipitate the halide by dropwise addition of silver nitrate solution with stirring. Allow to stand for about 20 minutes. Then filter through a 5 cm filter of medium porosity. Wash with water containing 3 drops of nitric acid per 100 ml. It is not necessary to remove the last traces of the precipitate from the beaker.

In the same beaker place about 100 ml of water, 5 ml of buffer pH 10, and dissolve 0·2–0·3 g of potassium tetracyanonickelate in this solution. Place the filter with the precipitate into that solution and stir until solution is complete. (Silver iodide requires a temperature of about 60°C.) Add murexide indicator and titrate with EDTA until the colour changes from yellow to violet. Observe all precautions for titration of nickel (experiment 14.7 (page 83).

Calculation: 1 ml 0·0100 M EDTA = 0·70906 mg Cl, 1·5982 mg Br or 2·5381 mg I.

Remarks: For remarks and some additional background information see experiment 16.4 (page 95).

CHAPTER 18

EXAMPLES OF MULTICOMPONENT MIXTURES

THE most desirable procedure for the analysis of a multicomponent mixture would be one in which titrations could be made con-
secutively. That is to say, one constituent is titrated at first, and
then after an appropriate change of the conditions, the next constituent is determined and so on. A few examples of such an elegant
procedure are known where the same indicator can be employed
for two constituents. Widespread application of this principle, however, is not possible because a second indicator has to be introduced
frequently, and its colour changes are then impaired by the presence
of the first indicator (only very few metallochromic indicators are
colourless in the unmetallized form!). The application of instrumental methods, however, offers here a distinctive advantage, because
the difficulties with indicators do not exist. In the majority of cases
involving multi-component systems it is necessary to use aliquot
portions in combination with pH-variation and masking.

Experiment 18.1: Consecutive titration of bismuth and lead.
Theory: The titration of bismuth using XO as indicator is readily
possible at a pH of about 1. Under these conditions lead neither combines with the indicator nor with EDTA. After the bismuth is titrated,
the pH is increased to about 5–6 where lead gives the brilliant red
XO-complex and also combines with EDTA. See experiment 7.20 (page 50).

Reagents: 0·01 M bismuth solution; 0·01 M lead solution; 0·0100 M EDTA;
XO 0·1%; buffer pH 5; Urotropine; universal indicator paper; dilute
ammonia; 1 : 2 nitric acid.
Procedure; Place 10–20 ml (exactly measured) of each of the bismuth
and the lead solution into a 500-ml beaker, add 1 ml of 1 : 2 nitric acid
and dilute with distilled water to about 300 ml. The pH should be

101

between 1 and 2. Check with indicator paper and, if necessary, adjust with dilute ammonia or nitric acid. Add 3–5 drops of indicator solution and titrate with EDTA until the colour changes from red to yellow. Let the burette reading be A.

Now add buffer pH 5 until the red colour of the Pb-XO complex appears. Check that the pH is between 5 and 6 and adjust if necessary. Titrate with EDTA until the colour changes again to lemon yellow. Let the burette reading be B.

Calculation: $A \times 2 \cdot 090 = \text{mg Bi}$

$$(B - A) \times 2 \cdot 0719 = \text{mg Pb}.$$

Note: With the amounts of metals as limited to the experiment, the pH will not fall sufficiently during the titrations to cause difficulties. With greater metal ion concentrations, however, control and readjustment of the pH during the titrations may be necessary. It is preferable to adjust the pH in the titration of lead with urotropine. High concentrations of acetate buffer cause the end-point to be less sharp. With much lead present pH-control is necessary, because the buffer capacity of urotropine is not particularly high. Urotropine may be added as the solid or as a 20% aqueous solution. The consecutive titration can be applied to other pairs, e.g. Bi-Zn or Bi-Cd. If more than one of these metals is present the second titration gives the sum of e.g. Pb + Zn.

Experiment 18.2: Determination of zinc and lead (magnesium, calcium, manganese).

Theory: There are two ways of determining zinc and lead in one sample. In the first a single solution is used and the two metals are titrated successively. Lead is titrated first, zinc being masked by addition of potassium cyanide. Then zinc is demasked with formaldehyde. According to the equation

$$\text{KCN} + \text{H}_2\text{CO} \rightleftharpoons \text{KOCH}_2 \cdot \text{CN} \tag{18.1}$$

cyanide reacts with formaldehyde yielding glycollic nitrile. This reaction takes place with the free cyanide as well as with that complexing the zinc.

In the second method the sum, lead and zinc, is determined first. Then potassium cyanide is added and the amount of EDTA liberated equivalent to the zinc is titrated with magnesium solution.

This experiment is an example of a general case; the same principle can be applied when zinc is accompanied by manganese, calcium, magnesium or some other less common metals.

Reagents: 0·01 M lead solution; 0·01 M zinc solution; 0·001 M EDTA standard solution; 0·01 M magnesium solution to be standardized;

potassium cyanide, 5 per cent, freshly prepared; formaldehyde, 5 per cent; Erio T indicator powder; tartaric acid; buffer pH 10; universal indicator paper; dilute sodium hydroxide; methyl red, 0·1 per cent in ethanol.

Preparation of the sample: Mix 30–70 ml of each of the lead and zinc solutions in a 100 ml volumetric flask, make up to the mark with distilled water and shake well. The total sum of the mixed solutions should not exceed about 90 ml.

Procedure A: Place an aliquot of the sample (say 25 ml) in a 250 ml conical flask. Add a spatula-end of tartaric acid and neutralize with sodium hydroxide, using 2 drops of methyl red indicator. Add 5 ml of buffer pH 10 and 5 ml of potassium cyanide solution. Add the Erio T indicator and titrate until the colour changes from violet to blue. Let the reading on the burette be A ml.

Add formaldehyde solution dropwise and with shaking until the red colour is restored. Then titrate again to blue. If the endpoint is not sharp add more formaldehyde and titrate until a further addition of formaldehyde does not restore the red. Check the pH and if it has dropped add buffer pH 10 or ammonia to restore the pH value to about 10. Let the final reading on the burette be B ml.

Calculation:

$$A \times 2\cdot0719 = \text{mg Pb}$$
$$(B - A) \times 0\cdot6537 = \text{mg Zn}$$

The calculation refers to the amount of zinc and lead in the aliquot. To calculate the total amount present in the sample the figures must be multiplied by $100/Q$ where Q denotes the ml taken as aliquot.

Remarks: For the first part of the determination observe all precautions for a lead titration as mentioned in experiment 14.3 (page 80). The demasking reaction is accompanied by another reaction between formaldehyde and ammonia giving urotropine.

$$6 \text{ HCHO} + 4 \text{ NH}_3 = (\text{CH}_2)_6\text{N}_4 + 6 \text{ H}_2\text{O} \tag{18.2}$$

This reaction removes ammonia from the system which can cause a considerable drop in pH, hence checking of the pH is essential especially near the endpoint. An unfavourable excess of formaldehyde is avoided by adding it dropwise.

Procedure B: Place an aliquot (say 25 ml) of the sample in a 250 ml conical flask, add a spatula-end of tartaric acid and neutralize with sodium hydroxide using two drops of methyl red as acid-base indicator. Add 5 ml of buffer pH 10 and Erio T indicator and titrate with EDTA until the colour changes from red to blue (or green due to the screening with methyl red). Let the reading on the EDTA burette be C ml. Add 5 ml of potassium cyanide solution and titrate with magnesium solution until the colour changes from blue just to red. Let the reading on the magnesium burette be D ml. Bring just to clear blue with a few drops of EDTA solution. The reading on the EDTA burette is now E ml.

Standardize the magnesium solution using about 20 ml according to the procedure in experiment 14.1, page 79. Repeat the titration and take the average.

Calculation: The molarity of the magnesium solution is

$$M_{Mg} = \frac{\text{ml EDTA} \times 0 \cdot 01}{\text{ml magnesium solution}}$$

$$(E \times 0 \cdot 01 - D \times M_{Mg}) \times 207 \cdot 19 = \text{mg Pb}$$

$$[D \times M_{Mg} - (-EC) \times 0 \cdot 01] \times 65 \cdot 37 = \text{mg Zn}$$

Remarks: Observe in the first step all precautions for a lead titration (experiment 14.3, page 80 and in the back-titration for a magnesium titration (experiment 14.1, page 79). To ensure a sharper endpoint in the second part of the titration, a manganese solution may be used for the back-titration instead of a magnesium solution.

Either of the procedures may be applied to a mixture of Zn-Mg, Zn-Ca, or Zn-Mn. The addition of tartaric acid is not necessary but ascorbic acid must be added when manganese is present.

Experiment 18.3: Determination of zinc and copper (nickel, cobalt).

Theory: The release of zinc from its cyano complex by reaction with formaldehyde is described in experiment 18.2, page 102). In strongly alkaline solution other metal ions (e.g. copper or nickel) are also released. However these other reactions take place very slowly. Thus in ammoniacal solution, before any appreciable amounts of copper or nickel are liberated the formaldehyde is removed by the more rapid reaction which yields hexamethylenetetrammine (see formula (18.2), page103). Therefore selective demasking of zinc (and cadmium) is possible if an excess of formaldehyde is avoided. This is best accomplished by drop-wise addition. The red colour of the Erio T-zinc complex then appears and the free zinc can be titrated. If some cyanide is still present (combined with the zinc) a sluggish endpoint is observed and a violet colour is obtained. The violet turns to red after a few more drops of formaldehyde are added. A sharp endpoint occurs only if all cyanide is removed (except that masking copper etc.). As pointed out in experiment 18.2 (page 102), the reaction leading to hexamethylenetetrammine formation consumes ammonia and the pH drops. Hence careful pH control is necessary.

Reagents: 0·01 M solutions of zinc and copper; 0·0100 M EDTA standard solution; buffer pH 10; Erio T indicator; 5 per cent potassium cyanide, freshly prepared; 3 per cent formaldehyde; buffer pH 5; 0·1 per cent PAN; ethanol.

Preparation of the sample: Place 30–60 ml portions (exactly measured) of copper and zinc solution in a 100 ml volumetric flask and dilute to the mark. The sum of the volumes of the two solutions should not exceed 80–90 ml.

Procedure: (1) Place a 25 ml aliquot of the sample solution in a 100 ml conical flask, add 5 ml of buffer pH 5, 4 drops of PAN and 25 ml of alcohol. Titrate until the colour changes from violet to yellow. The titration gives the sum of copper and zinc. Let *A* be the millilitres of EDTA required.

(2) Place another 25 ml aliquot into a 250 ml conical flask. Add 10 ml of buffer pH 10 and 5 ml of potassium cyanide solution. The sample solution must become colourless; if not add more cyanide. Add Erio T indicator and then formaldehyde dropwise with vigorous stirring. If the colour turns red, start titrating with EDTA until the colour becomes blue or violet. Add more formaldehyde dropwise; the red colour will return. Again titrate with EDTA. Proceed in this manner until addition of some further drops of formaldehyde does not change the blue any further and the endpoint is sharp. Let *B* be the millilitres of EDTA required.

Calculation:

$$B \times 0.6537 = mg\ Zn$$
$$(A - B) \times 0.6354 = mg\ Cu$$

The above calculation refers to the amount of zinc and copper in the 25 ml aliquots. To obtain the total amount multiply by 4 (if the total sample was 100 ml).

Remarks: Study carefully the explanation in the theoretical part of this experiment as well as the remarks on experiment 18.2 (page 102). The addition of formaldehyde should be done exactly as described. If no endpoint is obtained through some mishap, and copper has been released, repeat the titration with a new aliquot. Check the pH near the endpoint in the second titration. If necessary add some drops of concentrated ammonia to restore the proper pH. The titration can be applied similarly to the determination of zinc in the presence of nickel or cobalt. The titration of the sum of the metals must be done with copper-PAN as indicator as described in experiment 16.3 (page 94).

Experiment 18.4: Determination of calcium and magnesium.

Theory: One of the most widely used applications of the EDTA titration is in the determination of calcium and magnesium. It was probably the simplicity of this process which led to the rapid acceptance of EDTA in analysis. The sum of calcium and magnesium is titrated in one aliquot of the sample solution and calcium is titrated in a further aliquot in strong alkaline medium in which magnesium is precipitated as the hydroxide. Magnesium is then calculated from the difference. This principle is very simple but many difficulties can arise in its practical application.

The amount of magnesium which may be in solution for the successful application of the procedure is limited. Furthermore the precipitate of magnesium hydroxide can occlude calcium to an appreciable extent. This may be prevented by adding EDTA in excess of the calcium present and then precipitating the magnesium. Because calcium is thereby combined with EDTA, coprecipitation is avoided. The solution is then filtered and the excess of EDTA is back-titrated with a standard calcium solution. By such a procedure it is possible to determine 1 per cent or less of calcium in magnesite.

Another difficulty may be the poor endpoint of the calcium titration when murexide is used as indicator, and especially in presence of magnesium. Use of a comparison solution or application of a photometric endpoint effects considerable improvement. New indicators, however, have been found to give sharper endpoints than murexide and have replaced it in practice.

Since the determination of calcium has to be made in strongly alkaline solution (pH higher than 12) care must be taken during the preparation of the test solution to avoid introduction of ammonium ions. In their presence the necessary high pH cannot be attained. This makes special procedures necessary for the separation of iron, aluminium, manganese, etc., if a multicomponent system has to be analysed, because the usual ammonia precipitation cannot be applied. Through use of appropriate masking reagents, however, such a separation can often be completely avoided.

Reagents: 0·01 M calcium solution; 0·01 M magnesium solution; 0·0100 M EDTA standard solution; 2 N sodium hydroxide solution; buffer pH 10; murexide and Erio T powder indicators.

Preparation of the sample: Mix 30–70 ml (exactly measured) of each of the calcium and magnesium solutions in a volumetric flask and dilute to the mark with water. The total volume of the two solutions should not exceed 80–90 ml.

Procedure: (1) Place an aliquot (25 ml is suitable) in a 100 ml conical flask. Add 5 ml of buffer pH 10 and dilute to about 50 ml. Add Erio T indicator, warm to about 60° C and titrate with EDTA until the colour changes from red to blue. Let A be the millilitres of EDTA required.

(2) Place another aliquot in a 100 ml conical flask. Add 5 ml of 2 N sodium hydroxide solution and murexide indicator and dilute to about 50 ml. Titrate with EDTA until the colour changes from salmon-red to violet. Let B be the millilitres of EDTA required.

Calculation:

$$B \times 0.4008 = mg\ Ca$$

$$(A - B) \times 0.2431 = mg\ Mg$$

This calculation gives the milligrams of calcium and magnesium respectively in the aliquot. To obtain the total amount present in the sample the figures have to be multiplied by $100/Q$, where Q is the number of millilitres of the aliquot.

Remarks: Observe all precautions for procedures (1) and (2) which are described in experiments 14.1 and 14.5, pages 79 and 81 respectively. Read the theory and remarks of these experiments to ensure a complete understanding of the present procedure. If available Calcon (CI 202) may be used instead of murexide in the titration of calcium. This indicator is of similar structure as Erio T, but reacts at high pH with calcium. The calcium complex at pH 12 is red whereas the free indicator is blue. The colour change red to blue is considerably sharper than that of murexide.

Experiment 18.5: Determination of water hardness.

Theory: Permanent water hardness is usually determined by titrating the sum of calcium and magnesium and expressing it in terms of calcium. This is done according to procedure (1) in experiment 18.4 (page 106), using Erio T as indicator. Difficulties may occur if an insufficient amount of magnesium is present; the titration then gives a poor endpoint, because of the weakness of the calcium-Erio T complex. Magnesium-EDTA complex should therefore be added in any water hardness determination to ensure a sharp endpoint.

If the calcium and magnesium hardness have to be determined separately, procedures (1) and (2) experiment 18.4 (page 106), are applied and magnesium is calculated by difference. Since water will seldom contain only calcium and magnesium as cations, precautions must be taken to avoid difficulties caused by traces of other metals such as copper, iron or manganese, which will block the indicator. Suitable masking reagents should be added.

The amount of calcium and magnesium present in water can vary within wide limits. If the amount is not known approximately, it is advisable to conduct a preliminary experiment to obtain a rough idea of the amounts present, and to carry out the final determination on an appropriate amount of the sample.

If hardness determinations have to be done very frequently, it is advisable to prepare an EDTA standard solution of such a concentration that the reading on the burette expresses directly parts per million calcium (or hardness degrees) when a certain volume of water is titrated.

Reagents: 0.01 M EDTA standard solution; buffer pH 10; magnesium-EDTA complex (for preparation see page 71); Erio T indicator powder; potassium cyanide; ascorbic acid..

Procedure. Preliminary experiment: Place about 10 ml of tap water in a 100 ml conical flask, add 3 ml of buffer pH 10, 2–3 ml of magnesium-EDTA solution, a few crystals of potassium cyanide and of ascorbic acid, and Erio T indicator. Titrate with EDTA until the colour changes from red to blue.

Final determination: From the preliminary experiment, calculate the amount of water sample necessary to require about 15–20 ml of EDTA solution. Measure this amount of water exactly, add all the reagents as in the preliminary experiment and titrate. Let the ml of water sample be A and the ml of EDTA required be B.

Calculation:

$$B/A \times 40080 \times M_{EDTA} = \text{p.p.m. Ca}$$

Remarks: If very low amounts of hardness are to be determined it may be necessary to take large samples of water and to concentrate them either by enrichment with a cation exchanger (strongly acidic, sulphonated type) or by simple evaporation of a known volume.

If the temporary hardness is to be determined, the same sample may be titrated before the EDTA titration by the conventional acidimetric procedure. There is no need to boil off the carbon dioxide.

Experiment 18.6: Determination of magnesium, lead, zinc, and copper in one sample.

Reagents: 0·01 M solutions of lead, zinc, copper and magnesium; 0·0100 M EDTA standard solution; buffer solutions pH 5 and pH 10; Erio T indicator; PAN indicator; tartaric acid; 5 per cent potassium cyanide solution, freshly prepared; 3 per cent formaldehyde solution; ethanol; 10 per cent thiosulphate solution.

Preparation of the sample: Place 30–100 ml portions (exactly measured) of the metal ion solutions into a 250 ml volumetric flask and dilute to the mark. The sum of the volumes of the metal solutions should not exceed 230–240 ml.

Procedure: (1) Take a 50 ml aliquot of the sample solution and place it into a 250 ml conical flask. Add 5 ml of buffer pH 5, 4 drops of PAN indicator and heat to boiling. Titrate the hot solution until the colour changes from violet to yellow. Titrate slowly near the endpoint. (See precautions for experiment 14.9, page 85.) The titrations give the sum Pb + Zn + Cu. Let A be the ml of EDTA required.

(2) Place another 50 ml aliquot portion in a 250 ml conical flask. Add a spatula-end of tartaric acid and 5–10 ml of buffer pH 10. The solution must be clear; if not, add more tartrate. Add 3 ml of potassium cyanide solution. The solution must be colourless; if not, add more cyanide. Add Erio T indicator, and titrate until the colour changes from red to blue. The titration gives the sum Pb + Mg. Let B be the ml of EDTA required.

(3) Add to the solution remaining from the second titration 3 per cent formalin until the red colour reappears. Titrate with EDTA to blue or violet. Then add more formaldehyde dropwise and titrate if the red is restored. Proceed until a sharp endpoint is obtained and the addition of a few more drops of formaldehyde does not bring back the red colour. Carefully observe the precautions mentioned in experiment 18.3 (page 104). Let C be the reading of the burette.

(4) Take a further 50 ml portion and place it in a 250 ml conical flask. Add 5 ml of buffer pH 5 and then thiosulphate solution dropwise until the test solution becomes completely colourless. Add 1 ml of the thiosulphate in excess. Adjust the pH to 6·5 by dropwise addition of dilute ammonia (check with universal indicator paper). Add 50 ml of ethanol, 4 drops of PAN indicator and titrate with EDTA until the colour changes from pink to yellow. The titration gives the sum Pb + Zn. Let D be the ml of EDTA required.

Calculation: Schematically the results of the titrations can be presented as follows:

$$Pb + Zn + Cu = A \text{ ml}$$
$$Pb + Mg \qquad = B \text{ ml}$$
$$Zn \qquad\qquad = C - B \text{ ml}$$
$$Pb + Zn \qquad = D \text{ ml}$$

From this it follows:

$$(C - B) \times 0·6537 = \text{mg Zn}$$
$$(A - D) \times 0·6354 = \text{mg Cu}$$
$$(C - D) \times 0·2431 = \text{mg Mg}$$
$$(D - C + B) \times 2·0719 = \text{mg Pb}$$

The above calculations are for the aliquots taken. To refer to the total sample the milligrams obtained must be multiplied by an appropriate factor. The factor is 5, if 50 ml aliquots have been used from a 250 ml sample solution.

Remarks: Several points must be carefully observed during these titrations.

The titration in step (2) must be done slowly near the endpoint because a magnesium endpoint is involved (see experiment 14.1, page 79). Warming will increase the rate of reaction. If, however, the solution is warmed, proceed with the release of the zinc in step (3) only after the solution has cooled to room temperature. Otherwise, release of the copper present may occur and the indicator will then be blocked. Carefully observe the precautions for the release of the zinc in the presence of copper mentioned in experiment 18.3 (page 104). Thiosulphate masks copper(II) in slightly acidic solution. The copper is reduced to the monovalent state and complexed. However this masking must be effected before the addition of PAN because thiosulphate is not able to remove copper from the copper-PAN complex.

Zinc also forms a thiosulphato-complex, which is, however, considerably weaker than the EDTA complex. An excess of thiosulphate should be avoided, otherwise the zinc-PAN endpoint becomes poor. 5 ml of 10 per cent thiosulphate solution masks 0·25 millimole of copper (= 15·9 mg Cu).

Since the calculation is based on the differences, the titrations must be done very carefully because drop errors may be additive. It is advisable to run two complete sets of titrations, and to take their averages as the basis for the calculation.

Compare the time for a complete duplicate analysis with the time probably required to resolve this analytical problem by classical methods.

Experiment 18.7: Determination of magnesium (calcium, manganese, lead or zinc) in the presence of iron.

Theory: Magnesium and some other metals which do not react with cyanide can be titrated in the presence of iron if the latter is masked by transforming it into ferrocyanide. The procedure, however, is not so simple as the masking of copper, zinc or other metals.

The addition of cyanide can only be made in alkaline solutions which would cause precipitation of ferric hydroxide. To avoid this difficulty, addition òf tartrate is necessary. The reaction between ferric iron and cyanide in a tartrate-containing alkaline solution produces ferricyanide which oxidizes the Erio T indicator, hence the ferricyanide must be reduced to ferrocyanide. This reduction is a slow reaction and warming is necessary. Ferrocyanide is known to form insoluble salts with many cations, hence the solution should be diluted sufficiently, or a back-titration procedure should be applied to avoid this precipitation.

Each step in the masking of iron is accompanied by a colour reaction which enables the course of the process to be followed easily; hence this experiment possesses considerable instructive value.

Reagents: 0·01 M magnesium solution; 0·01 M iron(III) solution; 0·0100 M EDTA standard solution; buffer pH 10; dilute sodium hydroxide solution; potassium cyanide; tartaric acid; ascorbic acid; dilute hydrochloric acid.

Preparation of the sample: Mix a measured amount (10–30 ml) of magnesium solution and add iron(III) solution up to 50 ml. More iron can be tolerated without its interfering with the titration but larger amounts of reagents have then to be used than are specified in the procedure below.

Procedure: Neutralize the sample by dropwise addition of sodium hydroxide until a slight turbidity of ferric hydroxide persists. Add a spatula-end of tartaric acid. Note the colour turns to deep yellow (ferritartrate). Add 20 ml of buffer pH 10. The colour fades somewhat. Add two spatula-ends of potassium cyanide (about 0·2 0·3 g). The colour turns to deep yellow (formation of ferricyanide). Add about 0·1 g of ascorbic acid. Note that a dark, dirty-brownish colour forms: (mixed ferri-ferrocyanide). Heat the solution almost to boiling. Note that the colour changes to slightly yellow (pure ferrocyanide). Add Erio T indicator and titrate until the colour changes from red to green-blue.

Calculation: 1 ml 0·0100 M EDTA = 0·2431 mg Mg.

Remarks: If a turbidity occurs after the addition of the buffer, insufficient tartrate is present. The indicator must be added *after* the complete reduction of the ferricyanide, otherwise it will be partially or totally oxidized.

Calcium, manganese or lead can be determined in exactly the same way. Any zinc (or cadmium) present can be demasked later on according to experiment 18.2 (page 102). If copper is present it will also be masked. The demasking of zinc, however, then has to be effected in cold solution (see experiment 18.3, page 104).

CHAPTER 19

POTENTIOMETRIC TITRATIONS

(1) THE potential of a reversible redox system which reacts according to the equilibrium

$$\text{Ox} + n\,e \rightleftharpoons \text{Red} \qquad (19.1)$$

may be calculated using Nernst's equation

$$E = E^\circ + \frac{0 \cdot 059}{n} \log \frac{[\text{Ox}]}{[\text{Red}]} \qquad (19.2)$$

where [Ox] and [Red] denote the concentrations of the oxidized and reduced species respectively expressed in moles per litre. E° is the standard potential (measured if Ox and Red are present at unit concentration) and n is the number of electrons (e) involved in the redox reaction. The factor $0 \cdot 059$ is valid for 25° C and if the potential is expressed in volts.

In a redox system where both species form a 1 : 1 complex with a complex-forming substance, Y, the stability constants of the complexes are given by

$$K_{\text{Ox}} = \frac{[\text{Ox}\,Y]}{[\text{Ox}] \cdot [Y]} \qquad (19.3)$$

$$K_{\text{Red}} = \frac{[\text{Red}\,Y]}{[\text{Red}] \cdot [Y]} \qquad (19.4)$$

113

For a mixture with given concentrations of Ox and Red the potential, E, can be calculated according to equation (19.2). If now the complex-forming substance is added, the potential changes and the new potential of the complexed couple, E_c, can be obtained by expressing [Ox] and [Red] from equation (19.3) and (19.4) and introducing it into (19.2). The result is

$$E_c = E^\circ + \frac{0\cdot059}{n} \log \frac{[OxY] \cdot K_{Red}}{[RedY] \cdot K_{Ox}} \qquad (19.5)$$

If the stability constants of both the oxidized and the reduced species are sufficiently high, the dissociation of the complexes may be considered to be negligible. Then in a first approximation $[OxY] = [Ox]$ and $[RedY] = [Red]$. Expression (19.5) becomes

$$E_c = E^\circ + \frac{0\cdot059}{n} \log \frac{[Ox] \cdot K_{Red}}{[Red] \cdot K_{Ox}} \qquad (19.6)$$

If Ox and Red are present in unit concentrations then obviously also $[OxY]$ and $[RedY]$ are unity and the standard potential of the complexed couple is given by the formula

$$E_c^\circ = E^\circ + \frac{0\cdot059}{n} \log \frac{K_{Red}}{K_{Ox}} \qquad (19.7)$$

Comparing E° and E_c° it can easily be seen that their difference increases with an increase in the difference of magnitude of the values for the stability constants.

(2) In the iron(III)-iron(II) system and with EDTA as complexing reagent, the following data are given: $E^\circ = 0\cdot76$ V, $\log K_{Ox} = 25\cdot0$ and $\log K_{Red} = 14\cdot3$. Introducing these data into equation (19.7) the standard potential of the complexed couple FeY^{-1}/FeY^{-2} is calculated to be $0\cdot11$ V. Because iron(II) complexes so much less strongly than iron(III), the standard potential of the complexed couple is about 600 mV less than that of the

uncomplexed one. Iron(II) in the presence of EDTA is therefore a reducing reagent of considerable strength. This forms the basis for a potentiometric titration of iron(III).

An iron(III) solution always contains traces of iron(II). If a titration is done with EDTA and the potential is measured during the titration by a suitable device the following happens. At first the potential is high because of the high concentration of uncomplexed iron(III). As further EDTA is added the potential does not change rapidly because iron(III) is still present in large excess over iron (II). The ratio Fe^{+3}/Fe^{+2} (see Nernst's equation) is hardly affected. Near the endpoint, however, the concentration of the uncomplexed iron(III) becomes comparable with or even less than that of the iron(II) and virtually all iron(III) is complexed; finally the iron (II) also is complexed. A considerable change in the ratio occurs which results in a sudden change of the potential indicating the endpoint of the titration.

Experiment 19.1: Potentiometric titration of iron.

Reagents: 0·01 M iron(III) solution; 0·0100 M EDTA standard solution; 20 per cent ammonium acetate solution; dilute aqueous ammonia; dilute hydrochloric acid; pH-indicator paper.

Apparatus: Any type of potentiometer or any electronic pH-meter with a millivolt scale may be used. For details of operation see the instruction book provided with the instrument.

A smooth platinum wire serves as the working electrode with a calomel electrode as a reference electrode. The latter may be inserted directly into the solution or connected via a salt bridge according to the type of cell. Read the operational manual carefully and check all connexions before switching on the instrument.

Procedure: Place 20–30 ml (exactly measured) of the iron(III) solution into a 400 ml beaker, dilute to 100–150 ml, add 5 ml of the ammonium acetate solution and adjust the pH to 4–5 using either aqueous ammonia or hydrochloric acid; check with the universal indicator paper. Insert the electrodes and the stirrer and make the necessary connexions. Add EDTA in small increments. When equilibrium is attained, record the potential and millilitres of EDTA after each addition. Continue until a pronounced "jump" in the potential occurs and make a few more additions beyond this endpoint.

Calculation: Plot the millilitres of EDTA on the abscissa vs. the milli-volts (or scale divisions) on the ordinate. Draw the curve and locate the endpoint. If the addition of EDTA just before and after the endpoint has been effected in equal steps, plotting may not be necessary and the millilitres of titrant corresponding to the endpoint may be calculated by formula. For details of such a calculation and handling of titration curves in general, see the instruction book of the instrument or text books on electrometric titrations.

$$1 \text{ ml } 0.01 \text{ M EDTA} = 0.5585 \text{ mg Fe.}$$

Remarks: The titration can also be done within the pH range 2–3. However at lower pH values the equilibrium is attained slowly. In contrast at pH 5 a practically instantaneous adjustment of the potential occurs. At higher pH, however, iron(III) may hydrolyse despite the stabilizing effect of the acetate added. Therefore, in practice, suitable dilution is advisable. Do not warm the solution, and take care to start the titration immediately to avoid hydrolysis

The pH within the above range does not affect the accuracy of the titration. Of course the rate of attainment of the equilibrium, the height of the jump and the position of the titration curve relative to the potential axis are changed. At pH 4–5 the break in the endpoint is about 200–300 mV.

If the amount of iron to be titrated is completely unknown, the addition of small increments is tedious. The following expedient is helpful. Adjust the pH as described above, but before starting the ti-tration set aside about one-tenth of the solution. Titrate with EDTA in increments of about 2–3 ml, until the jump occurs. No recording of data is necessary. The solution is thus over-titrated. Now transfer quantita-tively the reserved part of the solution to the main portion and the potential jumps in the opposite direction. Complete the titration in 0.1 ml or smaller increments, if desired, and now record the data after each addition.

Experiment 19.2: Potentiometric titration of copper.

Theory: The copper(I)-EDTA complex is much less stable than that of copper(II). A copper(II) solution always contains traces of copper(I). Therefore the theoretical background of the titration of copper is exactly the same as that already described for iron(III). (See page 114.)

Reagents: 0.01 M copper solution; 0.0100 M EDTA standard solution; buffer pH 10.

Apparatus: As described in experiment 19.1 (page 115).

Procedure: Place 20–30 ml (exactly measured) copper(II) solution in a 400 ml beaker, add 5 ml of buffer pH 10 and dilute to about 100–150 ml. Insert the electrodes and the stirrer. Make the necessary connexions and titrate as described in experiment 19.1

Calculation: Locate the endpoint as described in experiment 19.1.

$$1 \text{ ml } 0 \cdot 01 \text{ M EDTA} = 0 \cdot 6354 \text{ mg Cu.}$$

Experiment 19.3: Potentiometric determination of bismuth, lead, nickel or aluminium using a back-titration with iron(III).

Theory: A direct potentiometric titration is only possible for a metal having a redox couple that is readily reversible (as in the two previous experiments) and a sufficiently marked difference in the stability of the EDTA complexes of the reduced and oxidized species. However, many other metals can be determined by a back-titration procedure using a standard iron(III) solution as back titrant. The voltage break during the back-titration is in the opposite direction to that of the direct titration, but the theoretical background of the procedure is exactly the same. As pointed out in chapter 10.1 (page 60), the "true" endpoint in a back-titration procedure is established when the slight excess of back-titrant is removed by adding the necessary amount of EDTA. In the electrometric method however the endpoint is located graphically and is therefore in the same position regardless from which side of the curve it was approached. No final adjustment with EDTA is therefore necessary.

Reagents: 0·01 M solution of the metal ion to be determined; 0·0100 M EDTA standard solution; 0·01 M iron(III) solution to be standardized; 20 per cent sodium acetate solution; aqueous ammonia; dilute hydrochloric acid; universal indicator paper.

Apparatus: As described in experiment 19.1.

Procedure: Place 10–30 ml (exactly measured) of the metal ion solution in a 400 ml beaker and add an exactly measured amount of EDTA so that it is in excess over the metal. Let the volume be *A* ml. Dilute to about 100 ml; after addition of 5 ml of ammonium acetate solution, adjust the pH to 4–5 with ammonia or hydrochloric acid using indicator paper. Insert the stirrer and the electrodes, make the connexions and titrate with iron solution until a sharp potential change indicates the endpoint. Continue with a few more additions beyond the endpoint.

Standardize the iron(III) solution by titrating in duplicate about 20 ml as described in experiment 19.1. Take the average of the two titrations as the basis of the calculation.

Calculation: Locate the endpoint in the standardization of the iron (III) solution and the determination of the metal according to experiment 19.1. The molarity of the iron(III) solution is:

$$M_{Fe} = \frac{\text{ml EDTA} \times 0 \cdot 01}{\text{ml iron(III)}}$$

The metal content is found if B stands for the ml of iron(III) solution used for the back-titration of the excess EDTA.

$$(A \times 0 \cdot 01 - B \times M_{Fe}) \times A.W. = \text{mg metal}$$

where $A.W.$ is the atomic weight of the metal being titrated:

$$Bi = 209 \cdot 00; \ Pb = 207 \cdot 19; \ Ni = 58 \cdot 71; \ Al = 26 \cdot 98$$

Remarks: If aluminium is determined after addition of EDTA and adjustment of the pH, the solution must be boiled for two minutes. This is recommended to ensure complete complexing (see experiment 15.2, page 88). The titration, however, has to be done at room temperature.

The titration of the above-named elements can be done without interference, in the presence of even considerable amounts of alkaline earths. In practice the method is also applied to the determination of the sum of iron plus aluminium.

Bibliography

(1) Potentiometric determination of certain cations by means of complexone III solutions.
R. Pribil, Z. Koudela and B. Matyska, *Coll. Czechosl. Chem. Commun.* **16**, 80 (1951).
(2) The (potentiometric) determination of copper by complexometric titration with EDTA.
R. Belcher, D. Gibbons and T. S. West, *Analyt. Chim. Acta*, **13**, 226 (1955).

CHAPTER 20

POTENTIOMETRIC TITRATION USING THE MERCURY ELECTRODE

(1) A direct potentiometric titration applying the usual technique (smooth platinum electrode) as described in chapter 19 is limited to those metals having a redox couple which is readily reversible such as iron or copper: however, nearly all metals can be titrated potentiometrically via a replacement reaction involving mercury(II)-EDTA.

The redox potential of mercury(II) at an electrode consisting of metallic mercury is given by the following equation

$$E = E^{\circ} + \frac{0 \cdot 059}{2} \log \; [\mathrm{Hg_{II}}] \qquad (20.1)$$

The subscript II denotes mercuric ion, to differentiate clearly from metallic mercury.

If the solution contains mercury(II), another metal ion, M, and EDTA, complex formation takes place. The stability constants of the two complexes are given by

$$K_{\mathrm{Hg}} = \frac{[\mathrm{Hg_{II}}Y]}{[\mathrm{Hg_{II}}] \cdot [Y]} \qquad (20.2)$$

$$K_{\mathrm{M}} = \frac{[MY]}{[M] \cdot [Y]} \qquad (20.3)$$

119

The concentration of Hg_{II} is calculated from (20.2) and that of Y from (20.3). If these values are introduced into (20.1) the result is

$$E = E° + \frac{0 \cdot 059}{2} \log\left(\frac{[M]}{[MY]} \times [Hg_{II}Y] \times \frac{K_M}{K_{Hg}}\right) \qquad (20.4)$$

The situation near the end-point (which is the interesting part of a titration curve) can be interpreted by this formula. To make a titration the test solution is adjusted to the proper conditions (pH, masking reagent, etc.) and a small amount of mercury(II)-EDTA complex is added (a few drops of a $0 \cdot 005$ M solution.) The term K_M/K_{Hg} is obviously constant. $[Hg_{II}Y]$ can also be considered as constant within the small range near the endpoint, since only a small amount is present. Thus it can easily be seen that the potential depends only upon the reaction $[M]/[MY]$. This ratio shows the greatest change in the immediate vicinity of the equivalence point exactly in the same manner as in a normal potentiometric titration, where the endpoint break is caused by the big change in the ratio $[Ox]/[Red]$. Therefore we obtain curves which are similar to those obtained when titration is done at a platinum electrode.

It should be pointed out, that according to the pH conditions and the presence of other complex-forming substances the constants involved in the above derivation are the apparent constants (see chapter 4, page 24).

(2) Various metals can be titrated at appropriate pH values within the range of about 2–11. pH 2 is the lower limit because at that point the dissociation of even the highly stable EDTA complexes becomes too great. At a pH value higher than 11 mercuric hydroxide separates.

At high pH values oxygen can cause difficulties owing to its reaction with metallic mercury, resulting in a somewhat distorted titration curve. Generally this is not very important. If, however, very small amounts of a metal are to be determined, a sharp endpoint is not obtained unless oxygen is removed by sweeping out the solution with nitrogen gas.

At a pH of about 6 or less, chloride ion interferes because of the formation of the very stable chloro complexes of mercury. There-fore, if a titration is done in this pH range, care must be taken to avoid addition of hydrochloric acid during the preparation of the sample; otherwise chloride ion (as well as other halides) has to be removed before the titration.

Because no complex forming indicator is involved the require-ments with respect to differences in stability constants are less rigid, and thus consecutive titrations can be performed. For example, bismuth may be titrated at pH 2, then lead at pH 5 and calcium at pH 10 in one sample solution.

Experiment 20.1: Determination of copper.

Reagents: 0·01 M copper solution; 0·0100 M EDTA standard solution; buffer pH 10; metallic mercury; 0·05 M mercury(II)-EDTA solution.

Apparatus: A potentiometer of any type may be used and operated according to the particular instruction book. Calomel reference electrode.

Mercury electrode: The mercury drop electrode (do not confuse with the dropping mercury electrode used in polarography!) consists of a J-shaped glass tube, having at the lower end a small cavity for the mercury drop. A platinum wire is sealed into the curved part of the tube to connect the drop with the instrument (figure 6). One mercury drop can be used for many titrations if rinsed with water between titrations.

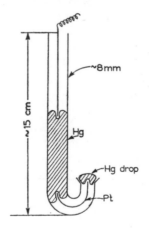

Figure 6. Mercury drop electrode.

The amalgam electrode is another type of mercury electrode. The construction can be seen easily from figure 7. A piece of gold wire about 5 cm long (the thickness is not critical) is connected firmly with a copper wire. The wires are then sealed into a glass tube (about 10 cm long and 0·5 cm in diameter) as shown in the figure, using de Khotinsky cement. About a 3 cm length of the gold wire is exposed. This free end is dipped into metallic mercury until it is completely silvery. Usually 0·5–1 min is sufficient. Avoid prolonged contact with the mercury otherwise the wire may dissolve.

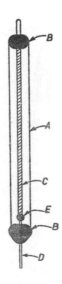

Figure 7. Gold amalgam electrode. (A) Glass tubing about 0·5 cm diameter. (B) de Khotinsky cement. (The cement may also cover the solder.) (C) Brass rod. (D) Gold wire. (E) Solder.

Procedure: Place 10–30 ml (exactly measured) of the copper solution in a 100 ml beaker. Add two drops of mercury-EDTA solution and 5 ml of buffer pH 10. Insert the stirrer, the mercury electrode and the reference electrode. Connect with the instrument according to the instruction book of the particular potentiometer. Start titrating in 1 ml increments and record the millilitres of titrant and the millivolts (or scale divisions) after every addition. Near the endpoint a slight increase of voltage is observed and from this point on add 0·1 ml portions of EDTA. Continue the titration until the potential is again nearly independent of any further addition of titrant.

Calculation: Plot millilitres of titrant on the abscissa, allowing 1 cm to represent each 0·1 ml titrant. On the ordinate, plot millivolts allowing 1 cm for 10 mV. A curve of the general shape shown in figure 8 will be obtained. Mark the points *a* and *b* where the linear part begins and ends. Read *a* and *b* on the abscissa and take the average of the two readings as the endpoint. Only the part of the curve in the vicinity of the endpoint needs be drawn.

$$1 \text{ ml } 0·01 \text{ M EDTA} = 0·6354 \text{ mg Cu.}$$

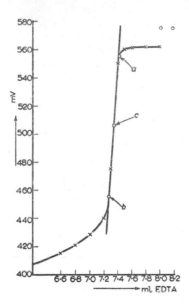

Figure 8. Potentiometric endpoint with a mercury drop electrode.

$$a = 7·42; b = 7·28$$
$$c - \frac{a + b}{2} = 7·35 \text{ ml}$$

Remarks: The curve in Figure 8 may go in reverse direction. In a potentiometric titration, absolute potential values are of no concern; rather potential differences are of interest, and hence no care need be taken to connect the cell in correct polarity to the meter. Further there is no need to plot mV; scale divisions of an uncalibrated meter will serve equally well. If very small amounts of copper are titrated, oxygen should be removed from the solution by passing nitrogen gas through it. The method can be applied to ultramicro amounts and surprisingly accurate results are obtained even with two ml of a 10^{-5} M copper solution. The height of the potential jump at the endpoint is somewhat dependent upon the pH and the concentration of the buffer. Be careful not to add too much buffer.

If the amount of metal to be titrated is completely unknown the method of setting aside a part of the solution may help to avoid over-shooting of the endpoint (see experiment 19.1, page 115).

By the above procedure other metals can be titrated, including calcium, magnesium, zinc, cadmium and mercury. Nickel complexes slowly and the attainment of a steady potential requires some time after each addition of EDTA. Lead, copper, nickel, cobalt and some other metals can be titrated in acetate-buffered solution at pH about 6. Under these conditions, care must be taken to exclude chloride (and other halides).

Bibliography

(1) Chelometric titrations with potentiometric endpoint detection. Mercury as pM indicator electrode.
C. N. Reilley and R. W. Schmid, *Analyt. Chem.*, **30**, 947 (1958).

(2) Application of the mercury indicator electrode in potentiometry.
R. W. Schmid, *Chemits-Analyst*, **51**, 56 (1962).

CHAPTER 21

PHOTOMETRIC TITRATIONS

(1) PHOTOMETRIC or colorimetric endpoint location is useful in EDTA titrations in the following cases:

(a) If no suitable indicator is available, but a colour change takes place during the formation of the metal-EDTA complex.

(b) If the colour change of the indicator is not easily seen visually.

(c) If the colour change at the endpoint is not sharp because of a low stability constant of the metal-indicator complex.

(d) If, for the sake of selectivity, a complex-forming indicator must be avoided (see chapter 8, page 51).

(e) If the solution to be titrated has such an intense colour of its own that any indicator is totally screened.

(f) If the concentration of the metal to be titrated is so small that it becomes comparable with that of the indicator.

A photometric titration may be done with or without an added indicator, and the theoretical treatment of the problem and the handling of the sample differs according to which of these particular conditions holds.

(2) Titration without an added indicator.

Some of the metal-EDTA complexes differ in their colour from that of the "free" metal or of any other complex present. For example, a copper sulphate solution at pH 4–5 is slightly greenish blue, whereas the solution of copper-EDTA complex at the same pH

125

shows a deeper blue. If, therefore, the absorbance is measured during the titration, a gradual increase in absorbance can be noticed until the equivalence point is reached. From that point on no further change occurs except by dilution with the titrant. If a rather concentrated titrant solution is used this effect becomes negligible. If millilitres of titrant are plotted vs. absorbance, graphs are obtained which consist of two straight lines. Their point of intersection marks the endpoint.

Various types of curves are shown in figure 9. The above-mentioned example of a copper titration at pH 4–5 gives a curve of type *a*. If, however, copper is titrated at pH 10 in ammoniacal medium, when the titration is started the solution has a deep blue colour (copper tetrammino-complex) which has a high absorbance. During the course of the titration the much lighter colour of the copper-EDTA complex develops and the absorbance decreases gradually and again becomes constant from the endpoint onwards; a curve of type *b* results.

Even two metals can be titrated successively in the same solution if their stability constants differ sufficiently (see chapter 8, page 51)

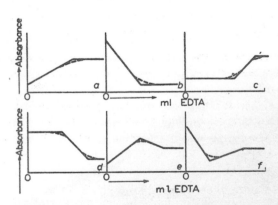

Figure 9. Various types of photometric titration curves (without metallochrome indicator).

and if the second metal to be titrated forms a coloured EDTA complex. A curve of type *c* or *d* may be obtained if the first metal titrated does not change colour during complex formation, or at least that colour change does not affect the absorbance at the wavelength chosen for the titration of the second metal. If both metals form coloured complexes and absorption of light occurs for both complexes at the chosen wavelength curves of type *e* or *f* are obtained.

A metal which does not show a colour change during the complex formation can be titrated by addition of another metal which does show a colour change. For example, bismuth ion which has no colour and gives a colourless EDTA complex can be titrated if some copper is added. During the titration bismuth complexes first and the photometric titration curve is a horizontal line. After all the bismuth has complexed, copper starts to combine with the EDTA and the absorbance is increased. The amount of copper need not be known and there is no need to proceed with the titration until all copper is completely titrated. Copper in this case can be said to be a "photometric indicator ion".

Titrations can also be done using the ultra-violet range, provided that any wavelength exists in that range, where the absorption curves of the "free" metal and of its EDTA complex differ sufficiently.

(3) Titration with an added indicator.

If an indicator is present during the initial addition of EDTA the "free" metal is complexed. In a plot of millilitres versus absorbance, this part of the titration curve will have no slope or only a slight one, depending on whether the formation of the metal-EDTA complex is accompanied by a colour change or not. (Part *a*, curve A, figure 10.) When all the free metal has combined with the EDTA, the next increments of titrant will begin to remove the metal from the indicator complex. This step is accompanied by a much larger change in absorbance (part *b*, curve A, figure 10). When all the metal is removed from the indicator any further addition of EDTA will not change the absorbance, except by dilution (part *e*, curve A, figure 10).

The type of curve which occurs (such as shown in figure 10) or the increase, depends upon whether the wavelength is chosen at the absorption peak of the free indicator or that of the metal-indicator complex.

In a titration which uses an added indicator only the part of the curve in the immediate vicinity of the endpoint and a small part beyond the endpoint is needed (the part which is formed when the indicator complex is titrated). Note that there is a difference in locating the endpoint in a photometric titration and a potentiometric titration, despite the fact that the two curves have quite a similar shape.

Depending upon the stability constant of the metal indicator complex and its ratio to that of the metal-EDTA complex, a more or less pronounced curvature will occur at both ends of the steep part of the curve, but generally, in all titrations it is possible to draw two straight lines.

It is especially important that sufficiently small increments of titrant be added within the range of the large absorbance change,

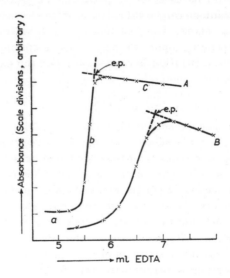

Figure 10. Typical photometric titration curves (with metallochrome indicator). (A) Nickel, murexide (green filter). (B) Calcium, murexide (orange filter).

so that this part of the curve can be drawn completely and without guesswork. For this purpose the method of setting aside part of the test-solution for a crude location of the endpoint is very helpful (see experiment 19.1, page 115).

Apparatus and general procedure: It is not possible to give instrumental details of the procedure, since there are many different types of photometer. For each type some variation in the arrangement is necessary. However, if the basic principle of the titration and the operating details of the instrument are understood, it should be a simple matter to carry out the titration.

The simplest way is as follows. Select and adjust the proper wavelength or filter. Use water as blank and set the absorbance to zero (=100 per cent transmittance). Then insert the cell with the sample and titrate in small increments. Record the absorbance and the burette reading after each addition.

This procedure, however, does not allow the full sensitivity of the instrument to be used in the particular range covered by the curve. This advantage can be gained by inserting the sample solution and using it as blank. The instrument is set to zero or infinite absorbance depending upon whether the absorption increases or decreases, and the titration is carried out. For the experiments in this book the simpler method is sufficient. For a detailed theoretical explanation of the more sensitive methods, any book dealing with instrumental analysis should be consulted.

Most of the instruments commercially available have cells so small that the sample solution cannot be placed in them completely. Changes in the design of the instrument or the use of special cuvettes are described by many investigators. This is not necessary to show the principle of the titration, and the following (admittedly tedious) methods can be applied. Titrate in any vessel of appropriate volume. After each addition of titrant transfer some of the solution to the absorption cell and measure the absorbance. After the measurement, return the contents of the cell to the main solution; add another portion of titrant; stir; transfer some of the solution to the cell; measure the absorbance and proceed in this manner until the titration is complete.

Each time the sample is transferred from the cell to the main solution, some drops will remain in the cell. It might seem that an error is thereby introduced; this is not so, because the titration is done with continued mixing until *all* the metal is titrated, thus giving the correct result.

To avoid a curvature in the titration graph, which may cause difficulties in locating the endpoint, a sufficiently concentrated solution of titrant should be used. Then the increments can be kept so small that the increase of the volume during the titration is negligible. A correction for the dilution effect can be applied but the calculation is tedious.

Experiment 21.1: Determination of copper without an added indicator.

Reagents: 0·01 M copper solution; 0·100 M EDTA standard solution; acetate buffer pH 5.

Apparatus: For photometer see above; micro burette 1 or 2 ml.

Procedure: Place 5–10 ml (exactly measured) of the copper solution in the absorption cell (or if that is too small in another vessel, see above). Add 3 ml of buffer pH 5. Adjust the instrument to a wavelength of about 740 mμ or use a yellow filter. With water as blank set the zero absorbance. Insert the sample and titrate with 0·1 ml portions. Apply an appropriate modification of the general procedure given above. Continue with the titration until the absorbance does not change after about five further additions of EDTA.

Calculation: Plot millilitres of titrant on the abscissa vs. absorbance on the ordinate. Draw two straight lines through the points and read the millilitres on the intersection. If a curvature occurs near the intersection use the points far from the curvature to construct the diagram.

$$1 \text{ ml } 0\cdot1 \text{ M EDTA} = 6\cdot354 \text{ mg Cu.}$$

Remarks: If a micro burette is not available use a macro burette and a 0·01 M EDTA solution. Under these conditions however the absorbance-readings must be corrected for dilution by multiplying each reading by the factor $(V_i + V_t)/V_i \cdot$ where V_i denotes the initial volume of the sample in millilitres, V_t is the millilitres of titrant added at that particular reading. The increments are increased to 0·5–1 ml.

Experiment 21.2: Determination of iron and copper in the same solution without an added indicator.

Reagents: 0·01 M copper solution; 0·01 M iron(III) solution; 0·100 M EDTA standard solution; acetic acid; aqueous ammonia; pH indicator paper.

Apparatus: As described in experiment 21.1 (page 130).

Preparation of the sample solution: Mix 10–50 ml (exactly measured) of each of the two metal ion solutions in a 100 ml volumetric flask and dilute to the mark with water. The total volume of the two metal solutions should not exceed 80–90 ml.

Procedure: Place 10–25 ml (exactly measured) of the sample solution in a cell or 100 ml beaker and adjust the pH to about 2–3 using acetic acid or ammonia. Titrate in exactly the same manner as described in the preceding experiment.

Calculation: Plot millilitres of titrant (abscissa) versus absorbance. Draw three straight lines. The first intersection (between the first horizontal and the ascending part) marks the amount of EDTA taken for the iron titration. Let the amount be A ml. The second intersection (between the ascending part and the second horizontal part) marks the millilitres required to titrate the sum iron + copper. Let this amount be B ml.

$$A \times 5\cdot585 = \text{mg Fe}$$
$$(B - A) \times 6\cdot354 = \text{mg Cu}.$$

Remarks: The calculation refers to the amounts in the aliquot portions. To obtain the total amount the results are multiplied by V_t / V_a where V_a and V_t are the volumes of the aliquot portions and the total sample respectively. At first the absorbance increases after each addition but goes down after some time. This is due to the fact that copper is complexed much more rapidly than iron. At first, with each addition of EDTA, the copper complex is formed immediately. The absorbance increases since the copper-EDTA complex absorbs at the chosen wavelength. Iron, however, has a much more stable EDTA complex and soon replaces copper. The yellow iron-EDTA complex does not absorb at the particular wavelength and therefore the absorbance decreases. Accordingly it is important to wait before recording the absorbance until equilibrium is reached. When all the iron has been titrated, this time effect disappears. Because only a few points are necessary for the construction of the titration curve, this time effect is not an aggravating factor.

Experiment 21.3: Determination of calcium using murexide as indicator.

Reagents: 0·01 M calcium solution; 0·1 M EDTA standard solution; 2 N sodium hydroxide solution; murexide indicator powder.

Apparatus: As described in experiment 21.1 (page 130).

Procedure: Take 10–15 ml (exactly measured) of the calcium solution, place it in a cell or beaker and add 5 ml of sodium hydroxide and some murexide indicator. Set the wavelength at 600–625 mμ or use an orange filter. Start the titration according to the appropriate modification of the general procedure. Use especially small increments in the range where the calcium is removed from the indicator complex.

Calculation: Plot millilitres of EDTA on the abscissa and absorbance on the ordinate. Draw a straight line through the steep part of the curve and through the second (nearly) horizontal part. The intersection marks the endpoint.

$$1 \text{ ml } 0·1 \text{ M EDTA} = 4·008 \text{ mg Ca.}$$

Remarks: It is strongly recommended that the expedient of reserving a part of the solution to be titrated be used (see experiment 19.1, page 115). Titrate in large increments until the solution is over-titrated. Add the reserved portion quantitatively and titrate in as small increments as desired to ensure a sufficient number of points on the steep part of the curve. It is very instructive to titrate micro amounts of calcium▾ Repeat the experiment but titrate only a few millilitres of 0·001 M calcium solution with 0·01 M EDTA.

Bibliography
(1) Photometric titrations.
A. L. Underwood *J. Chem. Education*, **31**, 394 (1954).
(2) Theory of photoelectric complex formation titrations using metal indicators.
A. Ringbom and E. Wänninen, *Analyt. Chim. Acta*, 11, 153 (1954).
(3) Photometric titrations.
J. B. Headridge, Pergamon Press, Oxford (1961).

APPENDIX A

QUESTIONS

(1) What are the requirements for a titration procedure based on complex formation?

(2) What is a bidentate ligand?

(3) What is a chelate complex?

(4) What is meant by the term "1 : 1 complex"?

(5) Which rings, formed during chelation, are the most stable?

(6) What is meant by the term "chelate effect"?

(7) What is a "zwitterion"?

(8) How can you easily differentiate experimentally how much of the calcium in the compound $Ca_2Y \cdot n\ H_2O$ is "salt-like" bound and how much is complexed?

(9) List some common trade names for EDTA?

(10) Which ions form coloured complexes with EDTA?

(11) What is a "hydroxocomplex"? Give examples.

(12) Do the colours of EDTA complexes depend on the acidity of the solution?

(13) Is the rate of complex formation with EDTA always high?

(14) Why should a solution always be well buffered during an EDTA titration?

(15) Does EDTA prevent all metal ions from being precipitated as hydroxides at high pH?

(16) What is the relationship between the dissociation and stability constant of a complex?

(17) What is meant by the term "apparent stability constant"?

(18) How does increasing acidity of a solution influence EDTA complexes?

(19) What is meant by the term "metallochrome indicator"?

(20) What are the requirements for a metal indicator?

(21) What are the colour changes of Erio T as an acid-base indicator?

(22) Describe the colour changes of the given indicators for the titration of the following metals:

Erio T: Mg, Zn, Cd, Pb; Murexide: Ca, Cu, Ni.

Pyrocatechol Violet: Bi, Cu, Ni. PAN: Cu.

(23) What are the colours of the murexide complexes of: Mg, Zn, Co?

(24) Explain why the colour change is green–yellow–violet at the endpoint when a rather concentrated copper solution in ammoniacal medium is titrated using murexide as indicator.

(25) Can Erio T be used as indicator in titrations in acid medium? Give reasons for your answer.

(26) Why is the colour change at the endpoint slow when copper is titrated using PAN as indicator?

(27) What is the advantage of adding alcohol or acetone when copper is titrated using PAN as indicator?

(28) What is meant by the term "blocking an indicator"?

(29) What is the advantage of Pyrocatechol Violet over Erio T as an indicator for titrations in ammoniacal medium?

(30) How can the selectivity of EDTA titrations be increased?

(31) What is masking and demasking?

(32) What is meant by the term "screened indicator"?

(33) What are the disadvantages of precipitation for masking purposes?

(34) Give an example of a reduction reaction used for masking purposes?

(35) What is the reaction between cyanide and formaldehyde in the demasking procedure for zinc?

(36) Why are copper, nickel and some other metals not demasked from their cyanide complexes by formaldehyde in ammoniacal solution?

(37) What is the cause of the drop in pH during the demasking procedure for zinc with formaldehyde?

(38) What types of titration can be differentiated?

(39) Give examples of methods for the determination of anions or organic substances?

(40) What is meant by the term "pendulum endpoint"? Discuss the advantages and disadvantages?

(41) What is a "partial replacement titration"? Give examples.

(42) Is the titre of an EDTA standard solution constant? Under what conditions? Which effects are important?

(43) What are the advantages of using the free EDTA acid as a primary standard?

(44) What are the common impurities of "distilled water" and how can they affect an EDTA titration?

(45) How should an EDTA standard solution be stored?

(46) Why is it important to check the pH near the endpoint in a titration which is done in strongly acid medium?

(47) When an EDTA titration is done in an unbuffered medium a decrease in the pH occurs. Explain why.

(48) When calcium is titrated at pH 12 using murexide as indicator why must the titration be started immediately and be done in a rather diluted solution?

(49) Describe the chemical reaction taking place during the preparation of potassium tetracyanonickelate.

(50) Can calcium be titrated with EDTA in acid medium? Give reasons for your answer.

(51) Explain what is the advantage of titrating Pb, Cu or Ni in acid medium.

(52) Work out a scheme (based only on EDTA titrations) for the analysis of solutions containing the cations listed below, in which only pH adjustment, masking, demasking and the use of aliquots are permitted. No separation is allowed.

(a) Fe-Ca-Mg. (b) Bi-Pb-Ca. (c) Zn-Fe-Mg-Cu. (d) Fe-Al.

(e) Fe-Pb-Zn.

APPENDIX B

PROBLEMS

(1) The stability constant of an EDTA complex is given as $K = 2 \cdot 5 \times 10^{18}$. Calculate the dissociation constant of the complex.

Answer: 4×10^{-19}.

(2) What is the concentration of uncomplexed metal in 10^{-3} M magnesium-EDTA solution and in a 10^{-2} M lead-EDTA solution if the stability constants of the complexes are 10^9 and 10^{18} respectively?

Answer: $[Mg] = 10^{-6}$ M; $[Pb] = 10^{-10}$ M.

(3) What is the concentration of free metal, M, in a solution containing the complex MY in a molarity 10^{-2}? The stability constant of the complex is 2×10^2. (Hint: the dissociation of a complex having such a low stability constant cannot be neglected.)

Answer: $[M] = 5 \times 10^{-3}$.

(4) Which CoY solution has the same molarity in free metal ion as a 10^{-1} M NiY solution?

$$\log K_{NiY} = 18 \cdot 62 \quad \log K_{CoY} = 16 \cdot 30$$

Answer: $4 \cdot 8 \times 10^{-4}$ M

(5) Equal volumes of a solution 2×10^{-2} M in lead-EDTA complex and of a solution 8×10^{-2} M in cadmium nitrate are mixed. What is the concentration of free lead and cadmium ion

137

respectively, if the stability constants are: $K_{PbY} = 10^{18}$ and $K_{CdY} = 10^{17}$? (Hint: Neglect dissociation of the complexes and assume that all free lead originates from the replacement reaction with the cadmium.)

Answer: $[Pb] = 4 \cdot 44 \times 10^{-3}$ M; $[Cd] = 3 \cdot 56 \times 10^{-2}$ M.

(6) A solution is 10^{-3} M in cupric ion and 10^{-1} M in ammonia and 10^{-1} M in EDTA. Calculate the β_A factor. Calculate the apparent stability constant of CuY if the absolute constant is $6 \cdot 3 \times 10^{18}$. Calculate the molarity of copper not complexed by EDTA. The stability constants of the copper ammine complexes are:

$$K_1 = 1 \cdot 50 \times 10^4 \quad K_2 = 3 \cdot 02 \times 10^3$$

$$K_3 = 7 \cdot 41 \times 10^2 \quad K_4 = 1 \cdot 29 \times 10^2$$

Answer: $\beta_A = 4 \cdot 8 \times 10^8$; $K_{ap.A} = 1 \cdot 3 \times 10^{10}$; $[M] = 7 \cdot 7 \times 10^{-13}$.

(7) Calculate the a_H factor for a solution having a pH = $6 \cdot 8$. Use the constants on page 17 and compare the result with that seen from the curve in figure 4 (page 26).

(8) The stability constants of the EDTA complexes of Co^{+2} and Co^{+3} are $10^{16 \cdot 3}$ and 10^{31} respectively. Calculate the standard potential of the complexed couple if the standard potential of the uncomplexed couple $E^\circ = 1 \cdot 84$ V. (Use $0 \cdot 060$ as factor in Nernst's equation.)

Answer: $E_c^\circ = 1 \cdot 02$ V.

(9) A metal in its oxidized form, O, and reduced form, R, forms 1 : 1 complexes with a complex-forming substance, Z. Calculate the stability constant K_{OZ} if the following data are given:

$R \rightleftarrows O + e$. $E^\circ_{O/R} = + 0 \cdot 700$ V. The potential of a solution containing $[OZ] = 4 \times 10^{-2}$ M and $[RZ] = 2 \times 10^{-2}$ M is $+ 0 \cdot 418$ V. $K_{RZ} = 10^{15}$.

Answer: $K_{OZ} = 10^{20}$.

(10) Two metals, M and N, form 1 : 1 complexes with a complex-forming substance, Y. The two stability constants are $K_{MY}=10^{18}$ and $K_{NY}=10^{17}$. A solution is 2×10^{-3} M with regard to MY and 10^{-3} M with regard to metal N. Calculate the molar concentrations of the following species present:

$$[MY], [M], [N], [NY].$$

Answer: $[MY]=5/3\times10^{-3}; [M]=[NY]=1/3\times10^{-3}; [N]=2/3\times10^{-3}$.

(11) A metal, M, forms a 1 : 1 complex with a complex-former Y and the stability constant of the complex is $K_{MY}=10^{18}$. A metal, N, in a concentration 10^{-3} is added to a 2×10^{-3} M solution of MY. The amount of metal, M, liberated was determined spectrophotometrically and found to be 2×10^{-4} M. Calculate the stability constant of the complex NY.

Answer: $K_{NY}=2\cdot78\times10^{16}$.

(12) A complex MY has the stability constant $K=10^2$. Calculate the concentration of free metal if

   (a) the concentration of MY is $C_{MY}=2\times10^{-2}$

   (b) $C_{MY}=2\times10^{-2}$ but Y is in excess of 10^{-2} (so $C_Y=3\times10^{-2}$!!)

   (c) Calculate the percentage of dissociation for both cases.

Answer: (a) $[M]=10^{-2}$; (b) $[M]=7\cdot3\times10^{-3}$; (c) $50\cdot0$ and $36\cdot5$ per cent.

AUTHOR INDEX

141

SUBJECT INDEX

Italic page numbers in connection with the determination of a compound indicate that a detailed procedure for the titration is given.

142